The Psychopharmacology of Legal Psychoactive Foods

Professor Massimo F. Marcone, Ph.D., C.Chem., Chimiste, FRSC (UK)

Department of Food Science

University of Guelph

Second Edition

NELSON EDUCATION

ISBN-13: 978-0-17-668470-9
ISBN-10: 0-17-668470-0

Consists of Original Works

Food as Carriers for Drugs
Massimo F. Marcone
© 2014

Cover Credit:

Jeffrey Collingwood/Shutterstock
Jaroslav74/Shutterstock

The Psychopharmacology of Legal Psychoactive Foods

Acknowledgements

I would like to thank all the hundreds of students who over the last few years
have inputted on the creation of this book..
This book is dedicated to them and
all the wonderful students who I have had the privilege of teaching over the years
and who have enriched my life in so many ways.

A special thank you goes to K. Moom and H. Thomsen
for their efforts in editing this book.

Grazie

A personal note from Dr. Marcone

It is my hope that all individuals reading this book will be challenged to re-examine how they view common foods and gain a deeper appreciation for the field of Food Science.

Professor M.F. Marcone, Ph.D., C.Chem., Chimiste, FRSC (UK)

Professor of Food Science
University of Guelph

It should be noted that any information contained in this book is
for educational purposes only and does not constitute an endorsement for the consumption of
any such foods described here-in, for any reason or purpose.
Furthermore, the information contained herein on any possible
associated psychoactive effects which may occur by their consumption are general in nature.
It does not cover all possible uses, actions, precautions, side effects, or interactions,
nor is the information intended as medical advice or for making an evaluation as to the risks
and benefits of consuming such food.

Class endorsement

"Professor Marcone is an inspiring teacher who is dedicated to student learning and success. Despite the challenge of effectively teaching several hundreds of students, Professor Marcone has captivated his students, sparking a desire to know more!
This, is a professor whose great enthusiasm towards teaching brought the classroom to life especially on the topic of psychoactive foods.
He has made this one course, a truly memorable experience.
It is safe to say that Professor Marcone's teaching is every bit as stimulating as the foods of which he teaches!"

- The Students of Principles of Food Science FOOD*2010, Winter 2010

FOOD**LAW**

Ronald Doering

Sweet dreams are made of cheese

Who am I to disagree?

nutmeg, if consumed in large enough quantities, can have powerful psychoactive effects providing a type of intoxication similar to the combination of alcohol and marijuana. Scientific studies show that ginseng is a safe and easy way to boost energy and some varieties such as Korean Red ginseng can so affect the levels of nitric acid in the body that it can increase blood flow including in the vaginal tissues resulting in enhanced sexual pleasure for women. Eating just two pieces of poppy seed cake will produce a positive result in drug tests as morphine will be detected in urine; repeated consumption of poppy seed tea can lead to morphine tolerance, dependence and finally addiction. Consumption of various species of fish can provide powerful hallucinations similar to LSD. While some of the 500 natural chemicals in a single piece of chocolate may have a psychotic effect on humans, the current state of the science is inadequate to support chocolate's aphrodisiac claims. These are just a small sample of the many interesting insights contained in Professor Massimo Marcone's latest book, *The Psychopharmacology of Legal Psychoactive Foods* (Nelson, 2014).

While modifiers of consciousness such as morphine are regulated by governments, society permits its citizens, whether by legislation or default, to use legal psychoactive substances such as

caffeine, alcohol and nicotine. As it turns out, many other common and legal foods can also have major psychoactive effects. As in his earlier book, Marcone, a University of Guelph food chemist, explains in layman's language the science of how so many common foods that contain chemicals that can cross the blood-brain barrier can produce profound effects on our central nervous system.

Marcone tells the story of Vin Mariani, a Bordeaux wine containing both cocaine from coca leaves and caffeine from kola nuts, a beverage that became so popular at the turn of the 20th century that it was strongly endorsed by Pope Leo XIII, Pope Saint Pius X, and U.S. President William McKinley. It was widely used by such notables as Sigmund Freud, Thomas Edison, H.G. Wells, Jules Verne and Queen Victoria. All major opera singers of the time used this "tonic," as did the kings of Norway and Sweden. Widely recognized as the precursor to John Pemberton's Coca Cola, millions of bottles of Vin Mariani were sold before the U.S. banned cocaine in 1914.

Marcone devotes a chapter to the fascinating history and chemistry of the once highly popular absinthe, an alcohol distilled from wormwood, green anise and fennel. When consumed in large quantities, absinthe produces profound hallucinogenic effects because it contains the chemical thujone, which is similar to the THC found in cannabis. His chapter

on the chemistry of chili peppers, our second most popular spice, reviews their remarkable endorphin-producing capability and concludes that chili peppers have significant medicinal potential.

Apologies to the Eurythmics aside, what's this about sweet dreams and cheese? Most varieties of cheese, including Stilton, Danish Blue, and aged Cheddar, contain a chemical called tyramine which acts as a dopamine. This causes the release of another chemical (norepinephrine) that increases the amount of time that is spent in deep sleep. Cheese also contains high levels of the relaxant tryptophan, which contributes to a natural high. Moreover, the bacterial and fungal cultures in ripe cheeses produce large amounts of biogenic amines with high psychoactive properties. According to the science summarized by Marcone, really vivid dreams can be induced by consuming a mere 20g just before bedtime. A 2005 study commissioned by the British Cheese Board revealed that blue veined cheeses such as Stilton can produce particularly powerful and bizarre dreams. My own study conducted with a group of friends provides rich anecdotal data for the effect of Stilton cheese on sleep.

Most food chemistry articles are either turgid academic papers inaccessible to lay readers or the superficial pap that passes as "scientific" writing in the popular press. Again, my friend Massimo has found a way to make food chemistry interesting without compromising good science. We need more of this. ●

Ronald L. Doering, BA, LL.B., MA, LL.D., is a past president of the Canadian Food Inspection Agency. He is counsel in the Ottawa offices of Gowlings. Contact him at Ronald.doering@gowlings.com

Comments

"With inimitable verve, wit, and zest, Professor Marcone serves up an often startling exploration of myths and marvels about familiar substances that a great many people blithely imbibe."

Massimo has hit a jackpot again! With congratulations and best wishes

- Dudley R. Herschbach, Nobel Laureate in Chemistry, 1986, Harvard University

"As wide-ranging as it is easy to read, Dr. Marcone's tremendously informative new book on psychoactive foods will leave you with a heightened appreciation for food and chemistry."

- Dr. Michael Tseng, Ph.D., M.D., Psychiatrist, Centre of Addiction and Mental Health, Royal College of Physicians and Surgeons Canada

"The psychoactive foods described in Dr. Marcone's book give a whole new meaning to eating. 'Medications' are not only dispensed by nurses but, as Dr. Marcone shows, may also come on a patient's meal tray. The book will surprise and delight you and will make you 'psychoactive' about the foods you eat."

- Helle Thomsen, B.A.Sc., M.Sc., Registered Practical Nurse (Ontario), Ontario College of Nurses

"Professor Marcone has done it again! Nobody writes about chemistry and food the way he does. Great read!"

- Ronald Doering, *Food Lawyer* and former *President of the Canadian Food Inspection Agency of Canada*

"Dr. Marcone has taken kitchen chemistry to new heights, literally! He uncovers the surprising number of mind altering drugs hiding in the cupboard, the breadbox, and the refrigerator. That spice rack is a lot spicier than you think."

- Bob McDonald, *Host of Quirks and Quarks @CBC, Science Journalist,* and *Author*

"The definition of 'psychoactive' is "affecting the mind." That is exactly what this book does; it makes me think that Dr. Marcone himself is, literally, 'psychoactive'."

- Dr. Jay Ingram, *Host of the Daily Planet (till 2011),* and *Science Author*

Table of Contents

Figures

"For unrestricted use, the West has permitted only alcohol and tobacco.

All the other chemical Doors in the Wall are labelled Dope,

and their unauthorized takers are Fiends."

Aldous Huxley

The Doors of Perception, 1954

Prof. Massimo F. Marcone ©2013

Preface

From time immemorial *Homo Sapiens* have always had a keen interest in finding and using substances or engaging in activities which induce an altered state of consciousness, *i.e.* to induce hallucinations, dreams, and visions, to communicate with the spirit world, to prophesy, to achieve a higher and/or clearer level of consciousness, to engage in activities which one would not do when in full control of one's faculties, *etc.* It has been suggested that such a desire is a primary appetite in humans just as strong for the drive to satiate hunger, thirst, and sexual desire. Even the seemingly innocent activities of children in a playground, *e.g.* swinging, sliding, or spinning, have been regarded as activities aimed at producing an altered state of consciousness, albeit not premeditated. Such activities such as dancing or other physical activities have also been used by many different cultures as a form of inducing a trance for 'divine' communication. But psychoactive experiences can also be achieved through the consumption of either natural or man-made chemicals which are capable of affecting the brain. Being able to cross the blood-brain barrier, these bioactive substances used in moderation usually cause temporary changes in various brain functions by primarily affecting the central nervous system (CNS), the part of the nervous system consisting of the brain, spinal cord, and the retina in the back of the eye. The effects of such consumption would lead to changes in one's behaviour, mood, cognition, memory, perception, consciousness, and learning. Many psychoactive substances produce changes in consciousness and mood which many find pleasant and advantageous but may be the subtle 'hook' which may lead to these substances being abused. Although some like caffeine do not lead to clinical dependency, others such as alcohol, nicotine, marijuana, LSD, and heroin do lead to clinical dependency as the user is unable to stop despite knowing the detrimental effects of the substance. In many cases, the recreational use of substances leading to dependency are responsible for a wide variety of social problems such as increased crime rates, murders, abusive and violent relationships, increased violence, not counting the personal physiological, psychological, and economic toll.

Ever since humans left their first indelible footprint in the soft earth they have devoted much of their time, energy, and other resources to this quest, in some cases sparing no expense and knowing no limits. Humans have used various means such as psychoactive substances, chanting, dancing, meditation, or subjecting themselves to other physical stresses (*e.g.* hunger, cold, or loneliness) to attain this 'altered state of consciousness.' Until the last few hundred years, the chemical means of such intentionally or unintentionally inducing a psychoactive event could only be realized by the consumption of the entire plant or animal material containing the desired drug, an act which usually produced other undesirable side effects as the source itself would, for better or for worse, contain other bioactive substances. Neither the knowledge nor the technology were available to completely, effectively and safely extract and purify these substances from their plant or animal sources. Many valuable and beneficial drugs such as analgesics, antibiotics, cardiac medicines, mood altering drugs, effective cancer fighting drugs, *etc.* were and still are extracted from plant leaves, bark, roots, flowers, fruit, seeds, or sap or from animal fluids such as venom from insects or toxins from sea creatures.

While most modifiers of consciousness such as morphine and marijuana are regulated by national governments, society has permitted its citizens, whether by legislation or by default, the free choice of using three legal psychoactive substances *i.e.* caffeine, alcohol, and nicotine. Today many people would not regard these three as psychoactive and as drugs but, in fact, that is what they are; drugs which have the ability to alter the state of human consciousness albeit temporarily. Seemingly benign, some of the legal psychoactive substances such as caffeine are not addictive although many people would say otherwise. It may be habit forming but is not clinically addictive, and hence neither tolerance nor dependency develops. Others such as alcohol (ethanol), nicotine, opioid (*e.g.* morphine, marijuana, cocaine, heroin, and some pain medications however, are addictive and have both tolerance and dependence characteristics. The addictive nature is very subtle, alluring, and deceptive, eventually leading to becoming entangled in a sticky spider web which may be very difficult from which to escape.

Coffee is one of the most popular beverages worldwide enjoyed by peoples of all cultures. Consumed either hot or cold, it is prepared by dripping hot water through the ground roasted seeds (*aka* beans) of plants belonging to the Genus *Coffea*. The coffee bean itself contains the water soluble alkaloid chemical caffeine which acts as a natural pesticide although it is only present in very small amounts in 'green' unroasted coffee beans. Contrary to urban legends, caffeine has a much greater stimulative effect on the CNS than either of its two cousins, theophylline (tea) and theobromine (chocolate).

Coffee has come a long way ever since it was discovered in Ethiopia thousands of years ago. Being tightly controlled by an Arab monopoly, coffee although popular in Europe, eventually became regarded by many Europeans as the devil's wine, not only for its 'mysterious' and unexplainable stimulative effects but especially as a result of the Crusades when anything from Arab origin or obtained through Arab hands was regarded as anathema! Being pressured by his advisors to ban coffee, Pope Clement VIII (16th century) drank a cup of coffee to determine for himself the ultimate fate of this 'devil's wine'. To the complete surprise of many, however, this rather simple and innocent act had quite the opposite effect, and coffee aficionados owe much to this pope who ended up baptizing coffee which essentially made it 'Christian', saving it from banishment and obscurity. Coffee was used by the wealthy Europeans as early as the 17th century and just like so many other exotic and mysterious foods and beverages, its acquisition not only gave them bragging rights but coffee consumption became associated with wealth and social standing, a symbol of power and class differentiation. Coffee eventually made it to the streets of Europe with the first European coffee house opening in Venice in 1683 which, just like the coffee houses in the Arab world, soon became a meeting place to discuss the politics of the day. It was in the Green Dragon, a local coffee house in Boston (Massachusetts, USA), that the infamous Boston Tea Party of 1773 was convened. The American colonists had simply enough with the sense of conventional British 'entitlement' as symbolized by the heavy taxation on imported goods, in essence taxation without representation. After much simmering, the pot boiled over in the coffee house, and the American colonists rebelled against the British by throwing taxed tea into the harbour ; an iconic event symbolizing the independent and 'modern' way of thinking in the American colonies. From then on, it is alleged that if a man ordered tea then he was a loyal British subject, coffee signified that he was a patriot. The famous insurance company Lloyd's of London started as a coffee house in 1688, being a place where captains found insurers for their boats full of commodities such as slaves, coffee, tea, chocolate, spices, silk, *etc.* Even to this day, people working at Lloyd's of London are called waiters, a throw-back to their historical roots.

Caffeine is the most widely consumed legal psychoactive substance in the world although most people would not think of it as such. While roasting is necessary to develop the flavour of the coffee beans, this process actually decreases the caffeine content, contrary to popular belief. While a safe caffeine limit is generally regarded to be 300 mg, the equivalent of 2-3 cups of coffee, many people unknowingly consume even more as it is added to some foods, beverages, and medications. Negative effects such as irritability, insomnia, diarrhea, and anxiety are usually not seen after the consumption of one cup of coffee consumed 6 hours or more apart in appropriate doses. Metabolized in the liver, caffeine reaches its highest concentration in the blood and brain approximately 30-40 minutes after consumption with a half-life of about five hours in most people with many factors influencing this generality.

Caffeine along other nutritive chemicals is classified as a nootropic substance, *i.e.* a substance capable of improving mental functions such as cognition, attention, memory, concentration, intelligence, motivation, and learning. While caffeine has many physiological effects it is most known as a CNS stimulant by increasing alertness and improving short-term concentration and memory. With such benefits one may want to consume more coffee than what is recommended although too much too quickly may actually have the opposite effect. Caffeine increases alertness by blocking a substance called adenosine which is involved in sleep regulation. Some studies have indicated that caffeine is able to improve the mood of both young and old people alike as well as alleviating mild to moderate depression, stress, and anxiety, common symptoms of our 'modern' fast paced sleep deprived consumer society.

Innumerable clinical trials have examined the health benefits of caffeine but a clear picture has not emerged as the results have been contradictory at best. While this may be so, studies do indicate that both unroasted (green) and roasted coffee beans also have a high amount of antioxidants capable of dilating or constricting blood vessels in various part of the body, affecting balance, and elevating blood glucose levels. While present in plants as a natural defensive pesticide, caffeine readily crosses into the brain and hence has been a popular ingredient in headache medicines for its ability to dilate cerebral blood vessels. But there may be other more important reasons to celebrate caffeine's ability to enter the brain as some studies have suggested that it may be able to protect the brain against Alzheimer's disease. While many people use caffeine as a stimulant especially as a wake-me-upper in the morning or for late night studying, its other physiological effects make it an effective drug in many prescription and over-the-counter medicines.

Caffeine, however, is not without controversy as the appropriateness of exposing children to the stimulating effects of caffeine. Part of the problem is the casualness with which society regards caffeine's effects almost viewing it as harmless for everyone. Having the status as 'generally regarded as safe' (GRAS) by The United States Food and Drug Administration (US FDA) as well as implicitly by regulatory bodies in many other countries, manufacturers of soft drinks have added caffeine to cola soft drinks ever since the invention of the 'soft' drink but this addition has now been extended to clear soft drinks. Also controversial are the hugely popular 'energy drinks' which are advertised heavily to the younger generations especially with the caffeine providing no other function that a stimulating 'energy' boost which comes from both the high caffeine and sugar contents ... on the other hand, soft drinks are not much different. What many people do not realize is that energy drinks exceed the caffeine limit specified by US FDA for soft-drinks and cola-type beverages. Some energy drink manufacturers have voluntarily removed the caffeine from their alcoholic energy drinks as the combination of a stimulant and intoxicating depressant is a very dangerous combination. But product manufacturers are very creative as they try to entice consumers to purchase their products. Soap and shampoo manufacturers have also added it to their products claiming that it can be absorbed through the skin but this claim has not been proven to date.

Regardless of caffeine's stimulating and expanding popularity and many diverse uses, alcohol (ethanol) is by far mankind's most popular psychoactive drug ever since its effects were discovered by accident. Mankind has been very creative and imaginative in using many different plant and some animal sources in the production of alcohol which is essentially is a clear liquid made by the fermentation or distillation of different grains, fruits, or even vegetables. Alcoholic beers are produced by fermenting the starches (carbohydrates) in grains, *e.g.* barley (beer), rye (rye beer), wheat (wheat beer), corn (chichi), rice (sake), millet (millet beer), buckwheat, and sorghum. Many of these grains are also used in the distillation of spirits, *e.g.* whiskey (barley), rye whiskey (rye), and Bourbon whiskey (corn). Likewise the flesh and the skin of many different fruits are also sources of fermentable sugars (carbohydrates) producing many different alcoholic beverages, *e.g.* grapes (wine), apples (apple cider), pears (perry), pineapples (tepache), plums (plum wine), bananas, and coconut (toddy) as well as the rhizome ginger (ginger ale, ginger beer, ginger wine) with the science and art of aging improving the final flavour. Fruit spirits include brandy, cognac, and vermouth (grapes), applejack (apples), pear brandy (pear), and arrack (coconut). Other fermentable carbohydrates used in the production of other alcoholic beverages and spirits include potatoes (potato beer, and vodka respectively), sweet potato, cassava, sugarcane juice or molasses (basi and rum), agave juice (pulque, and tequila, mezcal, raicilla), honey and sugar (mead), palm sap, and milk (kefir).

It has been hypothesized that the first beers were made accidentally thousands of years ago when tall wheat and barley crops would bend over and ferment in puddles of rain water puddle on the ground. Domestic animals such as horses would drink from the puddles and the intoxicating effects of alcohol would be amply clear to the human riders who would then, with curiosity as ancient as mankind, start drinking the 'altered' water themselves. Wine too was probably discovered in a similar manner with grapes dropping from the vines and fermenting in puddles of rainwater. Spirits produced from fermented beverages are further distilled to concentrate the ethanol content and to eliminate congeners, *i.e.* contaminant chemicals such as methanol (a poison to humans), butanol, and other alcohols. Consumption of these alcoholic beverages is regarded as pleasant, enjoyable even refreshing. While so, over consumption can result in a 'hangover' which is produced by a variety of factors including the toxic effects of ethanol, the presence of congeners, low blood sugar, and dehydration among others. As many people can attest, a hangover is not a pleasant experience as it can include headache, nausea, sensitivity to both light and noise, tiredness, a depressed mood, and thirst, usually experienced the morning after an evening or night of excessive alcohol consumption.

Alcohol affects every organ and tissue in the body and is considered to be an addictive psychoactive substance. Whereas caffeine is a CNS stimulant, alcohol has the opposite effect, *i.e.* it is a CNS depressant which is a psychoactive substance which temporarily decreases the activity or function of specific tissues and/or organs. The effects of short term alcohol consumption can have secondary physiological effects including the dilation of blood vessels which, in turn, can lead to hypothermia, especially dangerous on a cold day. The good news about moderate alcohol consumption is that it is associated with fewer strokes and a lower risk of coronary heart disease in both men over 40 and post-menopausal women. Long-term effects of excessive alcohol consumption are, however, not that rosy as chronic over consumption has serious permanent side effects including changes in both brain and liver functions. Excessive consumption has been linked with dementia (brain); alcohol induced fatty liver, cirrhosis of the liver, improper liver functioning, and the development of certain cancers in both men and women. The consumption of alcoholic beverages can even affect the fetus *in utero* during pregnancy causing fetal alcohol syndrome, the effect being irreversible. While some symptoms are immediately obvious at birth, others become more obvious as the child grows. Many people still believe that drinking alcohol will make you warm on a cold day as is often portrayed in popular movie culture but, in reality, alcohol consumption has the opposite effect.

By far the world's most favourite legal psychoactive drug is the alkaloid nicotine produced in the roots of tobacco plants (*Solanaceae* family, Genus *Nicotiana*) and then concentrated in the leaves during plant maturation. In one form or another tobacco has been smoked by humans since 3000 B.C. and, in the Americas at least, tobacco has been used in religious ceremonies as an entheogen by shamans or medicine men , *i.e.* a chemical used to see the 'god within'. Likewise, tobacco was traded with other indigenous peoples as well as to seal important agreements and 'contracts' among various Indian tribes of North America. But once Europeans landed on the shores in the Americas, it was not long before this New World plant along with its related cousins including tomatoes, potatoes, chili peppers and sweet peppers travelled eastwards to Europe across the Atlantic Ocean. Over the next few centuries, tobacco became very popular among the Europeans, not just as an important trade commodity but also as a medicine, eventually gaining the 'status' of a recreational drug which all socio-economic classes could freely partake. While the occasional consumption of tobacco probably did not cause any detrimental health effects to the indigenous peoples, the historical chronic consumption of nicotine by Europeans and Asians has resulted in serious detrimental and fatal health effects including lung cancer which was not known or recognized as a distinct disease until 1761. Traditionally a leading cause of death in men, deaths from lung cancer in men is actually falling but death rates are increasing among women who traditionally did not smoke on a regular basis until the 1930-1940s as it was a taboo. As deaths from lung cancers are generally falling in the developed world, the numbers are unfortunately rising in Asia especially China. Interestingly, nicotine by itself is not addictive but when combined with substances in tobacco smoke which prevent the breakdown of the neurotransmitter dopamine as well as other neurotransmitters like it, the nicotine becomes potentially addictive. Historically, nicotine addiction has been one of the most difficult chemical addictions to break, the difficulty often compared to that of either cocaine or heroin.

The one milligram of absorbed nicotine from just one average cigarette acts both as a relaxant as well as a stimulant and is the source of dependent-smoking behaviour. While the half-life of nicotine is approximately two hours, this is extended by the popular 'refreshing' and 'cooling' additive of menthol to cigarettes which inhibits the breakdown of nicotine. Nicotine readily crosses the blood brain barrier affecting the CNS in less than seven seconds after inhalation into the lungs by smoking. In the brain, nicotine increases the release of many different neurotransmitters and hormones which are responsible for nicotine's multifaceted effects. The increase in the neurotransmitter dopamine in the reward area of the brain results in the common feeling of euphoria often associated with smoking. Likewise, nicotine inhaled from tobacco smoke increases the activity of receptors in specific areas of the brain which are particularly sensitive to nicotine reinforcing the physiological and psychological effects of the nicotine. The increase in dopamine and other neurotransmitters like it such as serotonin, melatonin, epinephrine, and norepinephrine is not caused by increased production but rather by decreased breakdown as the tobacco smoke contains various substances which actually prevent the breakdown of these types of neurotransmitters. Additionally, nicotine also stimulates the sympathetic nervous system by releasing epinephrine from the adrenal glands located on top of each of the kidneys. Epinephrine is a natural and important chemical which acts both as a hormone and a neurotransmitter affecting many organs and tissues in the body although differentially. When stimulated by nicotine, the increased epinephrine increases the heart rate, contracts blood vessels, dilates air passages and contributes to the 'fight or flight' response of the sympathetic nervous system.

Interesting research has shown that smokers unknowingly adjust their inhalation depending upon the desired effect. Nicotine is rather a unique and different 'animal' compared to many drugs as can change from being a stimulant to becoming a sedative/pain killer based on increasing dosages. Smokers wanting to experience the stimulating effect of nicotine take short quick puffs which produces low levels of nicotine in the blood which, in turn, stimulates nerve transmission. At low doses, nicotine probably enhances the activities of both norepinephrine and dopamine in the brain. When smokers, however, want to relax they take deep long puffs producing a high level of nicotine in the blood which depresses the transmission of nerve impulses. At these higher doses, nicotine enhances the effects of both serotonin and opiate activity producing the stereotypical sedative and pain-killing effect. Chronic cigarette smoking as well as the use of other tobacco products such as cigars, pipe tobacco, chewing tobacco, tobacco gum, snuff, *etc.* decreases both the length and quality of life, being a major risk factors in heart attacks, strokes, chronic pulmonary disease, emphysema, and cancers of the lung, mouth, larynx, and pancreas. In the latter part of the 20th century, secondary smoke, *i.e.* the smoke inhaled by people in the vicinity of people smoking cigarettes or cigars, was also identified as a health hazard as it was also a major factor in the development of disease especially in children.

Coca and Cocaine

In addition to the three most commonly consumed psychoactive drugs as describe previously; there are other drugs often armed with greater perceived potency, a perception not only based on their psychoactive effects but more so by the fact that they are illegal for unregulated use in most countries. One such drug is derived from coca leaves, an alkaloid

chemical which was unregulated at the time and hence freely added to some foods and beverages

only one hundred or so ago years. The product was Vin Mariani, a Bordeaux wine containing

both cocaine from coca leaves and caffeine from kola nuts. To boost both reputation and sales,

this perfectly legal tonic received 'glowing' endorsements from a long list of 19th and 20th

century notables including Pope Leo XIII (*cf.* Figure 1 below)) and his successor Pope Saint Pius

X (*cf.* Figure 2, p. 22), Queen Victoria, Russian and European royalty, The Shah of Persia,

Sigmund Freud, Thomas Edison (*cf.* Figure 3, p. 22), United States President William McKinley

(*cf.* Figure 4, p. 23), Jules Verne, H. G. Wells,

etc.

Coca (*Erythroxylum coca*) is a plant

indigenous to north-western South America

where it has had a long and deep rooted

relationship with the native peoples. Grown

mostly in the mid-elevation slopes of

Columbia, Ecuador, Peru, and Bolivia, the

leaves of the coca plant contains many

different alkaloids including nicotine with the

most popular cocaine varying between 0.3-

Leo P.P. XIII.

His Holiness Pope Leo XIII.

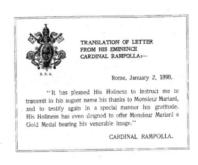

TRANSLATION OF LETTER
FROM HIS EMINENCE
CARDINAL RAMPOLLA:—

Rome, January 2, 1898.

"It has pleased His Holiness to instruct me to transmit in his august name his thanks to Monsieur Mariani, and to testify again in a special manner his gratitude. His Holiness has even deigned to offer Monsieur Mariani a Gold Medal bearing his venerable image."

CARDINAL RAMPOLLA.

FACSIMILE REPRODUCTION OF THE ORIGINAL LETTER AND GOLD MEDAL. SEE PAGE OPPOSITE.

1.5% by weight. Cocaine has both systemic and local effects which make its application as a

surface anaesthetic useful to this day.

Oral consumption as low as one gram

may cause death, and even lower doses of

> **Figure 1**
> A document endorsing Vin Mariani issued on behalf of His Holiness Pope Leo XIII in 1898. A gold medal was also awarded. Copyright of document owned by Professor M. F. Marcone. Copyright expired.

just 10 mg have been known to be fatal for some people.

Figure 2
A document endorsing Vin Mariani issued on behalf of
His Holiness Pope Pius X.
Copyright of document owned by Professor M. F. Marcone.

Figure 3
A document endorsing Vin Mariani issued on behalf of Thomas
Edison (best known for his invention of the light bulb) in 1892.
Copy of document owned by Professor M. F. Marcone.
Copyright expired.

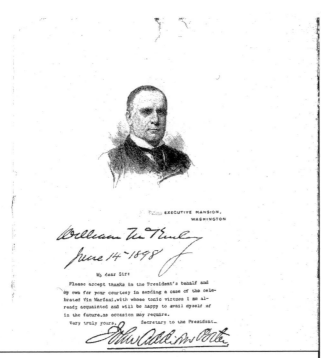

Figure 4
A document endorsing Vin Mariani issued on behalf of the 25th President of the United States of America (1897-1901) in 1898.
Copy of document owned by Professor M. F. Marcone. Copyright expired.

Coca has been consumed for thousands of years by the ancient peoples of South America who used it as an important part of Incan religion as well as revering it for its psychoactive effects. It was introduced during every ceremony (religious or warlike) to smoke the great offerings or for sacrifice. Coca (as the most important vegetal offering) was sacrificed during all religious festivals and the leaves were thrown towards the four cardinal points of the earth or burnt upon the altars. The Incas relied upon it heavily when consulting supernatural powers before taking any important action such as waging wars against other tribes, and they often used coca to help in predicting the outcome of these future events.

The discovery of ancient tools for both the cultivation and use of coca as well as sacks of coca leaves found within the tombs of mummies, reveal that many ancient South American tribes had been consuming coca for at least 3,000 years. A recent estimate shows that 90% of villagers in the areas where coca is cultivated still consume coca. Teens start off with daily consumption and continue right into old age with the average daily intake being 50 grams of leaves. The *coqueros* (coca users) moisten the wad of leaves with saliva and place the wad between their cheeks and gums. Then, a little lime (the ashes of the cereal quinoa; or the powder of crushed seashells) is added to the wad. The lime enhances the extraction of the cocaine and the related alkaloids from the leaves while accelerating their absorption into the bloodstream. The *coquero* chews and sucks on the leaves (just as a tobacco chewer would) and when all the juice has been extracted, he discards the wad, a process usually taking about 45 minutes. Part of the juice is absorbed directly through the oral mucosal membranes while the rest is swallowed and absorbed through the gastrointestinal tract (GI).

According to legend, the ancient South Americans received the coca from Manco Capac (the divine son of the Sun) to ease their lives on earth, and based on the effects of cocaine, this seems to be the case. Coca, it seems, invigorated the spirits of the *coquero* by triggering a release of energy (the typical *coquero* uses about 330 mg of cocaine daily). Additionally, consumption of coca provided many other benefits not associated with the psychoactive cocaine, as the average dose also fulfilled the *coquero's* daily vitamin requirements, especially of thiamine, riboflavin, and vitamin C. Chemical analysis has shown that coca leaves are relatively rich in vitamins, particularly thiamine, riboflavin, and vitamin C. In fact, chewing 50 grams of coca leaves would almost fulfill one's daily requirements of these three vitamins and considering that vegetables and fruits were greatly lacking in this part of the world, this became an important source. Also, there is evidence that coca has beneficial therapeutic properties: as it has been suggested that it can tone the smooth muscles of the entire GI tract, relieve gastritis, prevent diarrhea, vertigo, and vomiting; act as a respiratory stimulant, aid breathing during physical exertion, and prevent altitude syndrome (mountain sickness). Likewise it can also relieve fatigue of the larynx (hence the popularity of coca wines by both singers and public speakers alike). It can act as an antiseptic and an analgesic; it can help to recover physical strength and vital energy, regulate lipid and carbohydrate metabolism; and, as the longevity of many of the ancient South American tribes suggest, it can extend life expectancy.

Some well-known individuals including noted psychiatrist Sigmund Freud have written about their experiences with coca. For instance, Freud knew from his observation that responses to psychoactive drugs varied significantly amongst individuals: "I have had the opportunity of observing the effect of cocaine on quite a number of people; and on the basis of the findings I must stress, even more emphatically than before, the variation in individual reactions to cocaine. I found some individuals who showed signs of coca euphoria exactly like my own and others who experienced absolutely no effect from doses of 0.05-0.10 grams. Yet others reacted to coca with symptoms of slight intoxication, marked by talkativeness and giddy behaviour. On the other hand, an increased capacity for work seems to me to be a constant symptom." Although coca and cocaine are not the same, Freud did not experiment with coca leaves personally, and applied the terms "coca" and "cocaine" interchangeably. Freud also suggested several therapeutic applications for cocaine. He believed it was the best medication to alleviate the effects of alcohol and morphine addiction because cocaine made lethargic people and those with excessive pain and depression feel euphoric and energetic. Freud discovered that the stimulant properties of cocaine were ideal to relieve depression and he suggested that cocaine would be useful as a local anaesthetic.

In the late 1800s, coca leaves were placed in various types of alcohol beverages and then flavoured with various ingredients including kola nuts and various types of natural sweeteners such as sugar, honey, and molasses. Eventually, this 'brew' produced a drinkable beverage which became a popular mode for consuming both alcohol and cocaine. Unknown at the time, the cocaine dissolved in the alcohol is metabolized to the chemical cocaethylene (ethyl homologue of cocaine) which has a longer half-life than cocaine, and, according to animal studies, is more toxic. A review, however, concluded that using cocaine with alcohol does not create more cardiovascular problems than the additive combination of cocaine and alcohol. Given the longer physiological and more potent effects of this combination, alcoholic beverages containing cocaine became remarkably popular.

Vin Mariani-(Mariani Wine)

In the late 19th century, many performing vocal entertainers and opera singers used coca leaves to enhance their vocal range, versatility, and general stage presence. As he had read a recent scientific report about the effects of Peruvian coca leaves, a smart Corsican named Angelo François Mariani (*cf.* Figure 5 below) tried to make a commercial coca voice toner that would not involve a bulky mouthful of leaves, lime and saliva, and long periods of unpleasant and unacceptable cheek-bulging mastication.

ANGELO MARIANI
LE PROPAGATEUR DE LA COCA
1838-1914

Figure 5
A rare illustration of Angelo Mariani, the originator and formulator of Vin Mariani in 1863. His formulation is now recognized as the inventor of the precursor to Coca Cola.©
Copy of document owned by
Professor M .F. Marcone.

Given the fashionable Parisian divas did not want to look like clochards chewing plug tobacco; Mariani concluded, "This habit meets such an aversion nowadays in our countries that one has to find other methods to employ coca".

Mariani eventually came up with several methods but the most popular one was always his first attempt, the simplest being an alcoholic infusion. In the evening of April of 1869, Mariani was soaking a batch of Peruvian coca leaves in red Bordeaux wine

hoping the 24-proof alcohol solution would yield him a stable coca extract after it was boiled off

when a customer came unexpectedly into his laboratory apartment. She was a patient of his

physician cousin Charles Fauvel, a coloratura soprano who frankly was "known more for her

beauty than her talents". She had 'blown her throat out' with a command performance and, with

another performance shortly due, she was desperate for relief and begged Mariani for an

emergency voice restorative treatment. Mariani only had a kettle of leaves in mid extraction so

he bottled some for her in a pharmacy vial. The next night, she was said to sing like a

nightingale and sent a note to the Mariani's house, "It is excellent: You will send me a dozen

bottles". Unfortunately, the first hundred bottles of Mariani's products were literally too heavy

for the library shelves in his apartment. The bookcase collapsed and he lost his whole initial

investment but was fortunate that this had not happened before Dr. Fauvel observed the effects of

Mariani's new "Tonic Wine with the coca of Peru."

Mariani also had good marketing sense and knew that if he began putting his portrait in

Le Figaro and singing praises of his non-addictive, refreshing, and non-constipating new

nostrum, he would entice many of his high-society clients. Then, he came up with the brilliant

idea of getting others to literally sing his tonic's praises through a song. Apparently, one day, the

composer Charles Gounod visited Mariani's shop and asked him if he could charge a few bottles

of Vin Tonique as he'd left his cash at home. Being a clever businessman, Mariani used the

opportunity and told the famous creator of Faust that he could have all the coca wine he could

carry away if he'd compose a little song with the lyric "Vin Mariani" somewhere in it. That led

to the first advertising jingle which was jaunty and hypnotically mindless. Cleverly Gounod

composed a short jingle which ended on the same note that it began, and hence it just continued to go around and around in the head of anyone who heard it. Moreover, Mariani sent cases of Vin Mariani (50 grams of fresh coca leaves in each 500 ml of Bordeaux wine) to many celebrities and invited their appraisal.

The *Le Figaro* ads were very successful and all the included testimonials highlighted famous and well respected consumers. And what quality! Pope Leo XIII (*cf.* Figure 1, p. 19) and later Pope Saint Pius X (*cf.* Figure 2, p. 20) were two of them! Mariani received praises from Queen Victoria of Great Britain and Ireland, the Prince of Wales, the Kings of Norway and Sweden, the commanding general of the British Army, two popes, 16 heads of state and more than 8,000 physicians throughout the 23 years of published testimonials. Pope Leo XIII, after many years of sipping Vin Mariani, referred to Mariani as a "benefactor of humanity" and, being so taken with Vin Mariani, presented Angelo Mariani with a rare and much coveted Vatican gold medal, a sure sign of divine approval. In 1898, Cardinal Rampolla wrote, "It has pleased His Holiness to instruct me to transmit in his august name his thanks to Monsieur Mariani and to testify again in a special manner his gratitude. His Holiness has even deigned to offer Monsieur Mariani a Gold Medal bearing his venerable image". Adding more credence, Pope Leo XIII appeared on a poster in support of Vin Mariani, .a rare endorsement which is unheard of in papal history.

Pope (now canonized saint) Pius X was also one of the fans of this product as Cardinal Secretary of State Merry del Val wrote in 1904, "Most Illustrious Lord:, I will send to the Holy Father the bottles of coca wine assigned to him by Mr. Mariani. This shall certify that this is well-pleasing to His Holiness...."

United States President McKinley's personal secretary (a dedicated Marianic and 25th President of the United States) sent along heartfelt thanks from both of them after Angelo sent a few complimentary cases of Vin Tonique to the White House.

The Celestial Emperor of the ten thousand kingdoms of China and his bloody-handed "Bismarck of the East" General Li Hung Chang also drank it regularly. Princess Alexandra of Great Britain introduced her cousin the Czarina Alexandra of Russia to Vin Mariani. Although Russians maintained a total prohibition on other European wines and medicines, once Czar Nicholas consumed Mariani, he ordered cases of it from Neuilly in notes of gorgeously imperial arrogance. In the Kremlin Palace as well as in the Winter Palace banquet hall at St. Petersburg, only high important visitors with highest rankings were formally toasted with Vin Mariani à la Coca du Perou. The famous science-fiction author, Jules Verne who wrote *A Journey to the Centre of the Earth* wrote of this coca infused tonic wine, "Since a single bottle of Mariani's extraordinary coca wine guarantees a lifetime of hundred years, I shall be obliged to live until the year 2,700." Thomas Edison, a man who slept a mere four hours a day was also a steady user, and claimed that it helped him stay awake for longer hours. Queen Victoria was so happy to receive a set of Mariani testimonial volumes that she considered them among the finest specimens in her collection.

It was obvious that Mariani's wine elevated people in a way very different from regular alcohol, and it was not used only as medicine either. "Marianizing" was open and popular, and also evoked little shame. When the American Pure Food and Drug Administration (PF&DA) and the American Medical Association planned to monopolize the medicine market after 1900, somehow they could never find or even invent a Vin Mariani "addict" or overdose casualty. Although they wrote and publicized enormous amounts of misinformation about coca and cocaine but this was due to the so-called "mode of administration" in pharmacology. This remained so until about two decades ago when *in vitro* studies showed that the general scientific opinion about cocaine's activity was incorrect. It had been believed that cocaine was practically inactive when swallowed as the strong stomach acids would neutralize the cocaine. In 1978, however, Dr. Ronald Siegel (Neuropsychiatric unit, UCLA) discovered that after passing through the stomach, cocaine was reactivated after emptying from the stomach and was efficiently and quickly absorbed into the bloodstream across the mucosal barrier in the small intestine. Therefore the various effects of cocaine do not start until 30 minutes after ingestion, but there is no dramatic cocaine intoxication. The cocaine 'high', however, persists for over twice as long as snorting cocaine, but disappears very gently with no sudden dump-down into depression and replenished coke craving. If Dr. Siegel were to have tested the relative rates of absorption, metabolism, and elimination of all 14 coca alkaloids when administered orally together in a 24-proof alcohol-and-tannin suspension, it might be easier to understand some of the more bizarre testimonials to Vin Tonique Mariani à la Coca de Perou!

In the opinion of one Vin Mariani aficionado, "Vin Mariani may be called wine cordial medicament and a beverage as it is appreciated equally by husband, wife and child". Back in days when Vin Mariani was all the rage, children drank alcoholic beverages such as wine and beer with meals just as the adults since the water in most places was not safe to drink. And especially when they had wine with a little coca in it, the coca wine 'brightened' them and seemed to reduce their melancholies, improved their digestion, and stopped their coughing, a common medical complaint in people working long hours with not much food, drink or medicine while living in over-crowed squalor with no consistent heating, cooling or indoor plumbing. According to the standards of the time, Vin Mariani was a bonus to hospitals and orphanages everywhere especially to: "our little invalids," and "the little inmates of Villaponte". Angelo Mariani gave a free case of Vin Mariani Tonique to a nun, a Sister of Mercy who tended the Metropolitan Artist's Orphanage after she mentioned how "it revives and comforts my pale girls, rapidly giving them vigour and colour."

But Vin Mariani Tonique was not for the exclusive enjoyment of Europeans. Angelo Mariani had a production plant in the United States at 52 West 15th Street in Manhattan (New York) which was operated by his brother-in-law, J. Jaros. It was in The United States that Vin Mariani got into the worst trouble. In order to manufacture Vin Mariani, the company was importing large amounts of coca leaves from South America and Bordeaux wine from a firm in Europe, and then blending it all in Manhattan, similar to some current food products including wines much to the detriment of local farmers and producers wines. This innocent practice, however, was enough to smash Vin Mariani into the ground in the United States, practically ceasing all American production. The labels on the Vin Mariani bottles indicated that it was imported into the States which was true in one sense but yet false in another.

In 1906, that little technicality became the crux of contention when Dr. Harvey Wiley's new Pure Food and Drug Act (PF&DA) launched its well-intentioned but vindictive cocaine crackdown. Mariani and Jaros were condemned for technical violations of Rule Five of the new (PF&DA) which prohibited "misleading statements as to geographical source of the raw material, from which a product was made, or methods or collection or preparation". All this was only because Vin Mariani was being sold as an "imported" tonic while Wiley's sharp lawyers were able to charge that it was actually mixed in Manhattan.

In the same year, a full investigation into the nature and merchandising of Vin Mariani was launched and conducted by the American Council on Pharmacy and Chemistry with *The*

Journal of the American Medical Association (JAMA) giving this report top billing for their June issue. The venal patent-medicine witch-hunt conducted by the feds and The American Medical Association (AMA) in the first decade of this century was very thoroughly documented to warrant giving neither JAMA nor Wiley's PF&DA any credit for being sincere in their motives for trouncing Vin Mariani in print. Supposedly, JAMA was concerned with health-related matters yet their report focused solely on the mislabelling of the 'imported' product rather than on health matters.

There was no end to the demand of coca tonics as by 1915, over 10 million bottles of Vin Mariani alone had been sold. But Mariani was no longer alone in the coca wine line. Mariani's success was copied by dozens of competitors one of which was the Peruvian Wine of Coco (the misspelling was corrected later) offered for $1 per bottle in the 1902 Sears Roebuck catalogue. Angelo Mariani just continued making his coca wine tonic until his death in 1914, six months before the start of World War I *aka La Grand Guerre*, and eight months before the Harrison Act banned cocaine altogether in the United States. Vin Mariani always sold very quickly in places with less prohibition than the United States - anyplace where the Harrison Act was not enforced.

Coca-Cola

In 1885, John Pemberton copied Mariani's extraction method to make the American version of Angelo Mariani's Vin Tonique Mariani à la Coca de Perou. In the beginning where all things start, this beverage was a coca wine called Pemberton's French Wine Coca and was named Coca-Cola because it included the stimulants from coca leaves as well as kola nuts (the source of caffeine). Pemberton substituted caramel soda water for Bordeaux and added kola-nut extract for a special exotic pick-me-up. Initially, Coca-Cola was indeed true "dope" for its drinkers.

While its kick may have been legendary, America's favourite 'soft' drink (compared to a 'hard' beverage containing alcohol) once truly was "the real thing". Pemberton called for five ounces of coca leaves per gallon of syrup, by all accounts a significant dose! Later in 1891, Pemberton's son claimed his formula and altered extensively from Pemberton's original, the new version containing only a tenth of original amount of coca leaves. At its height, Coca-Cola once contained an estimated nine milligrams of cocaine per cup (*cf.* Figure 6 below).

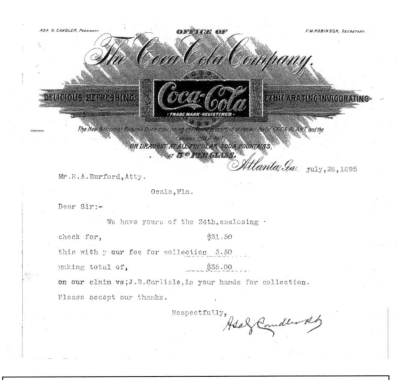

Figure 6
An extremely rare document owned by Professor M.F. Marcone,
dated July 25, 1895.
This document is signed by the president of Coca-Cola Company,
Mr. Asa A. Chandler and is one of the few documents which
clearly illustrates that the Coca-plant (*i.e.* the active ingredient of
cocaine) was intentionally used in the formulation of Coca-Cola

*Reproduction prohibited without the express written consent
of Professor M. F. Marcone.*

35

In 1886 after prohibition legislation was passed Pemberton not wanting to lose his profit making product sought ways to still produce his beverage while being in adherence of the law. It was then that he developed a new non-alcoholic formulation of the French coca wine. The original recipe was a mixture of water and coca-laced syrup without carbonated water with the fizz coming later when Pemberton accidentally added carbonated water *(aka* club soda) into a drink he had prepared for some friends. His friends enjoyed this new combination and thus Pemberton decided to keep using carbonated water. He initially sold the drink as a patent medicine for five cents per glass which became popular in the United States because people believed that carbonated water conferred beneficial effects on their health. Subsequently Coca-Cola's "brain tonic", produced for the nonalcoholic 'dry' market, was first bottled in 1894. During the first eight months only nine drinks were sold daily. The containers were sealed with corks which made a popping sound when pulled that paved the way to the name 'soda pop'. It was claimed that Coca-Cola could cure many diseases including morphine addiction, dyspepsia, neurasthenia, headaches, and impotence.

Around the end of the 19th century, campaigning to ban cocaine began in America and leading medical journals and newspapers published disgraceful racial bigoted, and downright false and misleading articles associating cocaine use with the "black" population. Stories came from the Southern States about the superhuman strength, cunning, and efficiency displayed by "black" coke users. "Bullets fired into vital parts, that would drop a sane man in his tracks, fail to check the "fiend"-fail to stop his rush or weaken his attack." The *New York Times* published a story of a police officer from North Carolina who fired his heavy army model handgun ("large enough to kill any game in America") directly into the heart of a "black" coke fiend which "did not even stagger the man". Therefore, top senators and representatives were guaranteeing for the open record. After 1904, Coca-Cola began using "spent" leaves (the leftovers from the cocaine-extraction process with cocaine trace levels leftover at a molecular level) instead of using fresh leaves. Today, a cocaine-free coca leaf extract (prepared by Stepan Company in New Jersey) is still used as an ingredient in Coca-Cola.

Today, The Stepan Company remains the only manufacturing plant authorized by the United States Federal Government to import raw Peruvian and Bolivian coca leaves and process it. Stepan Company buys about one hundred metric tons of dried Peruvian coca leaves annually. Other than making the coca flavoring agent for Coca-Cola, it also extracts cocaine from the coca leaves, and sells it to Mallinckrodt, the only pharmaceutical in the USA licensed to purify cocaine for medicinal applications.

AGWA - the Comeback of Coca Leaves

Angelo Mariani's Vin Tonique Mariani à la Coca de Perou metamorphasized into other similar or remotely related products, a phenomenon continued with many other foods and beverages when they 'landed' on American shores, *e.g.* pizza. Other alcoholic beverages infused with cocaine is the Bolivian Agwa de Bolivia (AG WA) a coca leaf spirit containing 37 different herbs and botanicals including coca leaves, ginseng, Chinese green tea, and cucumber. This light green fluorescent liquor with a sweet, dry finish coupled with a long lasting peppery bite won the gold medal in the World Spirit Awards in 2009. In the same year, it was chosen as the best in the Herbal Liqueur Category at the International Wine and Spirit Competition as well. The manufacturer (BABCO Europe Ltd., Amsterdam, Netherlands) claimed that the cocaine alkaloids of the coca leaves are removed during the production just as fit is or Coca-Cola, and that this spirited alcoholic beverage does not contain any traces of cocaine. The United States

Food and Drug Administration as well as the European Union Narcotics Commission have both approved Agwa de Bolivia for sale and consumption in their respective countries.

Conclusion

Throughout history and for various purposes, humans have been using psychoactive substances to alter their state of consciousness. Whether by choice or chance, caffeine, alcohol (ethanol), and nicotine have been accepted and continue to be the three most universally used, legally available, and socially acceptable psychoactive drugs in the world although in some countries they are not permitted due to religious beliefs. It seems conceivable that one of the reasons these drugs became socially acceptable was their consumption within food carriers in addition to the fact that the psychoactive effects were not deemed by society to be extreme. What makes these drugs so popular for human consumption is their accessibility through everyday foods and other carriers that offer, in addition to variety, other benefits of consumption through carriers such as reduced toxicity, alterations in drug metabolism, and potentially a controlled-release over time. These substances, however, have various beneficial and detrimental physiological and psychological effects in humans. The reasons for their consumption vary from one individual to another, and the mystery of that choice continues to be a topic of great research.

And, now what about other commonly consumed foods? Are there other everyday foods or beverages which can also induce an altered state of consciousness? If you dare, turn the next page and start reading! When finished with this book, then go to your food pantry and open the doors. You will be totally surprised and amazed at what you have unknowingly been consuming all these years, all without your knowledge or awareness. What psychoactive foods are lurking in your food pantry? Open your pantry, enjoy the feast!

Note:

It has been said that fact is always stranger than fiction as sometimes the truth just sounds too incredible. Aldous Huxley, author of Brave New World, prolific writer, philosophical mystic, and pacifist in the 20th century, was a strong advocate for the recreational use of psychedelic drugs. He participated in experiments on mescaline (a psychedelic alkaloid) which were conducted by Canadian psychiatrist Humphry Osmond who was the first to use the term 'psychedelic'. It was in response to his liberal attitude toward drug use and society's attitude towards them that Huxley wrote *The Doors of Perception* (1954), a quote from which introduces this exposé on current everyday foods in your food pantry and mine, foods which need to come 'out of the closet', to 'come clean' once and for all … they are psychoactive.

§ 1:

Absinthe

Getting high on the green fairy in the bottle

It was a lot of work but you have finally arrived at your overseas study semester …

destination '*jolie*' Paris! Standing on the balcony of your student residence you can see the

infamous Seine River meandering slowly through the city with the Eiffel Tower standing watch.

Paris, just like any loved child, has many nicknames with the most well-known being 'La Ville-

Lumière' *aka* 'The City of Lights'. Many people believe that this nickname originates from all

the street lights in the city. While this is true in more recent times, the nickname dates back

hundreds of years to the time of the Enlightenment (mid-17th century) when Paris became

famous as a center of enlightened education, quite fitting for this study semester abroad. The

city is spread out at your feet waiting for you to explore her, calling you to open the vault of her

many treasures as you turn from one street corner to another. Eagerly you look forward to your

formal studies but, quite honestly, you are more enthused about all the extra-curricular activities

this opportunity provides. Inhaling deeply and then exhaling with great satisfaction, this is

almost surreal ... you have to pinch yourself just to assure yourself that it is indeed real.

The bustle of early city traffic makes its way through the open balcony doors but the

noise is not noise, rather music to your ears. Having a few days before the start of formal

studies, you and your international house mates have decided to explore and get to know your

temporary home away from home. On this particular day, the group is headed via subway to

Montmartre in north central Paris to get a taste of *La Vie Bohemè*.

This 18th arrondissement of Paris is called "Martyrs Hill" as it was on this hill that St.

Denis, the first bishop of Paris, and some of his companions were beheaded for their Christian

faith in the 3rd century. Built on the hill which was baptized and made holy with their blood, the

foundation stone of the great white *La Basilique du Sacré Coeur* (Basilica of the Sacred Heart of

Jesus) was blessed in 1875. During the approximately 40 years of construction, *La Basilique du*

Sacré Coeur rose like the legendary phoenix from blood and ashes, from sacrifices, sweat, and tears, a sign of hope in a darkened corner of the world. Located well away from some of the most popular tourist attractions such as La Cathédrale Notre Dame, Le Tour Eiffel, and La Musée du Louvre, only the most determined make it to this holy ground in the heart of this bustling Bohemian neighbourhood. Rooted deeply in Paris' tallest hill, *Sacré Coeur* seemingly stretches without any effort up to Heaven, dominating the city's skyline. Greeting visitors from countries near and far with its dominating white dome, the basilica has a spectacular panoramic view of the city of lights lying at its feet.

The Archbishop of Paris requested that the *Basilique du Sacré Coeur* be built for the purpose of remembering the many lives that were lost in the Franco-Prussian War in 1870-1871. Issues in France were thought to be attributed to spiritual causes, so the Basilica was created to give thanks to Christ when the war was over. Today, this sacred place is still a widely visited place by Christians and non-Christians from many different countries. Indeed this ground is holy too as Saints have also put their footprints into this very earth, spiritual footprints which still remain: Saints Clotilde, Germain, Bernard of Clairvaux, Joan of Arc, Ignatius of Loyola, François Xavier, and Vincent de Paul. In the mid to late 1800s, this region of Paris was home to many different controversial artists. These artists enjoyed going to cafés nearby to discuss current issues, paint, write, or get inspired by the green muse, *aka* the green fairy, from drinking their favourite beverage, Absinthe, during *l'Heure Vert, aka* The Green Happy Hour.

It was said that the green muse would be present each time Absinthe was served. She would make her presence known every day during the hours between 5-7 pm, but rarely left on time. In Montmartre, the sickly smell of Absinthe would penetrate the air heavily as the green muse would entertain late into the night, meeting up with "friends" in backyard cafés and alleyways. Since Montmartre lies on the outskirts of Paris, alcohol was not subject to taxation which encouraged the green muse to linger longer. Many of her acquaintances would therefore stop by to meet and sit in her company for a while.

After a full day of soaking in the Bohemian atmosphere, the aroma of food entices you to sit at an outdoor patio of a nearby café. While resting, you continue to think about Absinthe and the green muse, and wonder if at one time long ago, the green muse would visit some of her talented and famous friends in the very spot you are sitting. Here she met many of her fans including royalty, artists, painters, novelists, poets, actors and actresses, stage performers, musicians, 19th century socialites, and 'wild men and women'. The most famous place for artists and rowdy individuals to encounter the green muse, however, is long gone. The notorious café *Le Chat Noir* (The Black Cat) was located in Sacré Coeur, and was only open from 1881-1897. Also located nearby in the red light Pigalle district is the infamous Moulin Rouge (Red Mill) which initially was a high class brothel. Eventually, Moulin Rouge was transformed into a fashionable nightclub. Immortalized by the paintings of Toulouse-Lautrec, many world class entertainers were headliners here; including Maurice Chevalier, Edith Piaf, Sammy Davis Jr., Pearl Bailey, Louis Armstrong, Frank Sinatra, and Elton John. Considered to be the home of the Can-can and the striptease, it is also known for its risqué shows, well at least risqué for the late 19th century.

After letting your mind wander, you look at *le menu* written '*en français*' and you hope that you will remember just enough high school French to order *un petit dejeuner*. Desiring something refreshing and invigorating to drink you ask the maître d' for his recommendation, something which reflects the spirit of the neighbourhood. "Ah, oui (Ah, yes)," replies the maître d', "I know exactly what the monsieur (mister) would enjoy. This drink has been served here for well over one hundred years, a drink of gentlemen and artists." After a few minutes he returns putting a beautiful glass with an emerald green beverage on the table in front of you which is topped with a gorgeous silver slotted spoon on which a sugar cube delicately balances. "Monsieur, I would like to introduce *La Fée Verte. Elle est une trés belle femme* (she is a most beautiful lady), and a good friend to many." Slowly and very deliberately he pours ice cold water over the sugar cube and, almost like magic, the drink becomes milky white. "Monsieur, may I introduce you to Absinthe. I hope you will enjoy the beautiful green muse, enjoy her friendship and the memories she brings." After just one drink, you can now begin to understand the reason she became the subject of many paintings, novels, poems, and tumultuous relationships.

Genuine Absinthe, the ultra-chic drink of "*La Belle Époque*" appealed to many with its natural green emerald colour, its ambiance of danger and seduction, and its allegedly psychoactive effects, which have caused a lot of controversy. The light green drink is made by steeping dried herbs, including some common wormwood (Artemisia absinthium), in ethyl alcohol and then distilling the steep liquor. The distillation is essential as wormwood contains extraordinarily bitter compounds called absinthins that must be excluded from the distillate. Fortunately, absinthins are alcohol insoluble, while the rest of the essential oil evaporates with alcohol vapour. In the early 20th century, the temperance movement spread across Europe and Absinthe was regarded as the source of all social evils. While Absinthe was all the rage in Paris during the 1850s, it received the unwanted nickname "the queen of poisons" by the early 20th century. It was then blamed for an increased number of people in insane asylums, trade union unrests, the women's emancipation movement, and increased crime rates. Absinthe took a lot of criticism across Europe, but it was not the only type of alcohol or substance of addiction in trouble. *Vin Tonique Mariani,* a cocaine-infused Bordeaux wine, was also extremely popular. Addiction is not a new "20th century" problem. In Europe in the 1800's, alcohol based elixirs and tonics were very prevalent. Vin Mariani was a French wine infused with cocaine which made it very popular, along with other legal "medicinal" substances such as morphine and opium.

Besides being very addictive, these substances were also psychoactive. Addictions were fairly common, but rarely mentioned in public. The green liqueur Absinthe was referred to as the green curse due to its high alcohol content. It was targeted by the temperance movement and was eventually banned by many countries in Europe and America by 1915.

The popularity of Absinthe hadn't caught on in America except for the city of New Orleans, Louisiana. In this particular city, the drink was infamously sold under the counter even though no foreign Absinthe was available. During the prohibition from 1920-1935, Absinthe devotees ensured it was still accessible because even when the prohibition was repealed, Absinthe was still not approved for importation.

Back in Europe, the temperance movement was on-going even though the consumption of French wine symbolized France's nationalism. By 1910, the French were drinking 36 million litres of Absinthe per year, as compared to their annual consumption of almost 5 billion litres of wine. With consumption of Absinthe increasing, the French wine makers became jealous and released a nasty campaign against the green muse from which the drink has yet to recover. In an attempt to gain Absinthe's popularity back, Pernod and Sons re-introduced an anise flavoured drink in 1951. Compared to Absinthe, however, this new drink was sweeter, had lower alcohol content, and most importantly it contained no wormwood. The French embraced the modern green muse and it once again visited the café society of France. It was only in the year 2000 that *La Fée Verte* was released from its bottled prison as the ban on Absinthe was lifted. The

European Union, however, is still uncertain about the sources and amounts of ingredients in Absinthe and therefore many countries have imposed restrictions on its alcoholic content.

Absinthe is a highly alcoholic spirit distilled with the three main ingredients: grande wormwood (*Artemisia absinthium*), green anise, and Florence fennel. These ingredients provide the base and flavour of the drink while the addition of other herbs and spices such as liquorice, star anise, angelica root, hyssop, and sweet flag reduce the bitter taste. Once the herbs are added to the alcohol they dissolve and the chlorophyll within the herbs changes the originally clear beverage into Absinthe's distinct green shade. The name Absinthe, even though highly disputed, has strong links to the Greek root word αψίνθιον *(apsinthion)* which means wormwood or some speculate it actually translates to undrinkable. This very bitter spirit was first developed by an exiled French doctor Pierre Ordinaire living in 18th century Switzerland. It was here that he used this 'Extrait d'Absinthe' as elixir for his patients who kept coming back for more due to its remarkable abilities.

The recipe for Absinthe eventually made its way into the hands of Henri Pernod, via some clever business techniques. Henri Pernod was the founder of Pernod Fils; a company which opened its first distillery in 1805. In the 1840s, the French military were prescribed wormwood mixed with wine to prevent malaria and other diseases while in Algeria. This was done because wormwood has the ability to kill parasites in the body and has a strong antimicrobial activity. These components were used to reduce the bitter taste of Absinthe when they returned home to France. Absinthe increased in popularity, especially in the years of blight when there were not enough grape crops to produce sufficient wine. With its new demand, the price of Absinthe dropped as many new producers started making the beverage. Some producers even made a fake

Absinthe by adding flavouring to ethanol and mimicking its colour by using heavy copper salts and clouding the drink with ammonium trichloride.

Eventually, Absinthe became cheaper than a bottle of Cognac (a famous type of brandy) making it possible for the working class to consume the drink almost daily. The growing popularity of Absinthe developed into a drink that was commonly consumed by both gentlemen and ladies alike while on an evening out. In addition, it was used as an *aperitif* before dinner in polite society. The alluring green muse was believed to impart a particular clarity to the mind while the person was intoxicated, hence its attraction to artists and musicians of all types. Furthermore, it became the symbolic drink of the Bohemian way of life, essentially giving 'the one finger salute' to the oppressive bourgeois monarchy disdained by so many. Between 1874 and 1910, the consumption of Absinthe in France alone increased from 700,000 litres to 36,000,000 litres per year! This profound increase in consumption resorted in France importing the drink from other countries.

Initially drunk straight out of the bottle, a stylized ritual of its service eventually evolved into what it is today, its enjoyment being a social occasion. The sugar (cube) was added later to reduce Absinthe's bitterness especially for the taste buds of 'refined' ladies. Additionally, the cold water numbed the taste buds as well as diluting the bitterness while extending the beverage. As with the ever changing world of fashion, Absinthe fell out of fashionable society by the late 19th century and disappeared from most café societies being replaced by another fashionable tonic drink, Vin Mariani. Produced by a French chemist in 1863 as a tonic to cure all ills, it was essentially a French Bordeaux wine infused with Peruvian coca leaves, the alcohol dissolving the cocaine from the bruised leaves. Imagine being drunk and high at the same time! Finally Vin Mariani gave those who consumed it an altered state of consciousness, a seductive 'high' that so many craved but eventually were caught in its tangled web of misery which, comparatively, was much worse than that of Absinthe.

Interestingly, the psychoactive alcoholic Vin Mariani eventually made its way to the United States where it inspired competition including the original Coca-Cola™ which during prohibition in Atlanta (Georgia) in the late 1880s was forced to reformulate into a non-alcoholic beverage. No company, including Vin Mariani, was able to legally import coca leaves after 1914. Regardless, the refurbished Mariani tonic no longer contained active narcotics or alcohol after 1910. But I digress, let's get back to Absinthe. Although the drink was sometimes associated with madmen, lunatics, and degenerates, many famous historical drinkers who simply had to meet the green muse drank it as well. The green fairy professed to clear and open their minds to new and unimaginable literature, art, music, and thought. Without the green muse, the world of art, literature, and music would not be as rich, but the cost for all this beauty was extremely high and personal.

Absinthe has a very high alcoholic content by volume, about 45 to 75 percent, so its products should be used wisely only by those who have a high alcohol tolerance. Present day Absinthes, although containing the same alcohol content, are less bitter since the thujone content taken from wormwood oil is now regulated by both the European Union (EU) and the United States, and the bitter taste is due to high thujone levels. The US regulations state that the thujone level must be less than 10 parts per million in order for the product to be labelled "thujone-free," which will allow the distribution of "Absinthe" labelled products. The EU regulation regarding the thujone content, however, varies according to the type of product it is used in, and with standardized amounts. Foods and beverages containing sage, however, are permitted to have higher amounts of thujone, as sage may contain up to 50% thujone. The maximal thujone level in alcoholic beverages is determined by the alcohol content. In the United States, another factor on the regulation of the thujone content in foods and beverages is dependent upon their content of Artemisia species, white cedar, oak moss, tansy or Yarrow root. Food or beverages containing any of these ingredients must be thujone free as the United States Department of Agriculture (USDA) has different approaches than the Europeans in regards to thujone regulations. Sage and sage oil are two substances that are generally regarded as safe (GRAS) even though they may contain a high thujone content. Thujone has its maximal limits within the food and beverage categories, while maintaining that any alcoholic beverages must be thujone-free (considered "thujone-free" is less than 10mg/kg). This thujone-free content of any alcoholic beverages is a mandatory requirement which extends to all Absinthe liquors imported in to the United States.

Ever since Absinthe started to gain a negative reputation, there has been much debate as to the causes of the hallucinogenic experiences associated with it. Absinthe's craziness has been associated with a disease called Absinthism, and as well, associated with addiction, hyper-excitability, tremors, convulsions, and hallucinations. This new disease was alleged to be able to pass from mother to child, but these suggestions were proven false by medical science, soon leading to the rejection of this so-called "Absinthism" disease as well. Suggestions have been made claiming that the alcoholic content in Absinthe is the cause behind its attributed effects, but this claim does not hold true, as alcohol is a central nervous system depressant, not stimulant.

By regulating the presence of thujone in food and beverages and by omitting it entirely in Absinthe (and other alcoholic beverages), it implies that thujone is still thought to be the cause of hallucinations and other known effects of the central nervous system. Skeptics maintain, however, that these effects are the result of over-exaggerated claims by those who deal with the promotion and sale of Absinthe. Thujone comes from wormwood oil, and in extreme quantities, has been pegged as a toxic substance that can cause seizures in some individuals. Early studies conducted on Absinthe and its hallucinogenic effects were not executed to the same degree, scientifically, as they are today. In the 1970s an article was published that claimed the hallucinogenic effects were caused because thujone has a similar molecular structure to tetrahydrolcannabinol (THC), a chemical found in cannabis. Years later this research was discredited when researchers concluded that thujone does not target the same receptors in the brain as THC. There is still controversy over this topic, as articles have been presented that support this original THC similarity hypothesis. An example, a graduate student from the Medical College of Virginia Commonwealth University writes, "It is also believed that the hydroxyl group of THC molecule and the carbonyl of thujone may interact at the same site. Modeling studies show a good degree of overlap." The absolute cause of the hallucinations and seizures that can be experienced following consumption of Absinthe is unknown due to the fact that previous studies differ in results and are therefore inconclusive. The alcohol distillation process in the 19th century removed any impurities/congeners, including chemicals that can cause changes in flavour and aroma that could contaminate the end product. It was the unprincipled makers of imitation Absinthe, however, that added toxic chemicals to common distilled alcohol. In a nut shell, the imitation Absinthe was a clear distilled alcohol similar to vodka, but to give it the infamous green tint, toxic and poisonous chemicals such as copper salts, antimony trichloride and artificial food colouring were added. As a result, the addition of these chemicals added to Absinthe's hallucinogenic effects on the consumer. For example, antimony trichloride was used to enhance the louche effect in Absinthe. The louche effect is commonly used to determine the 'grade' or quality of Absinthe, thus making it more appealing for imitators to add chemicals like antimony trichloride. The louche effect is the gradual change in opaqueness for Absinthe as it changes from natural green to a cloudy white when water is added. In the 19th century, it was boasted that Absinthe contained 260 - 350 mg/L of thujone. These results were skewed due to the fact that other compounds were misread as thujone via gas chromatography. Gas chromatography is the process by which compounds are turned into vapours to separate the individual chemicals for analysis. In 2008, 13 bottles of Absinthe from 1895-1910 were tested with modern chemical analysis and found that they only contained 0.5- 48.3 mg/L which averaged 25.4 mg/L over the 13 bottles.

The difference comes from the fact that modern analytical techniques are able to separate all the different types of thujone, making the 20th century product more advanced and better. High concentrations of thujone can have a significant effect on the mind and mental processes occurring in the brain by blocking chemicals from sending signals that are involved with controlling nerve impulses. When there is no control of nerve impulses, the brain becomes over-worked with nerve impulses constantly moving from one side of the head to the other, at the same time, causing hallucinations. The uncontrollable impulses also cause involuntary contraction of muscles, called muscle spasms as well as uncontrollable shaking of the body, called convulsions. Present day Absinthe produces the characteristics of alcohol intoxication, but with no hallucinations since the wormwood from the Absinthe before it was banned have been removed. Many Absinthe enthusiasts claim that these modern day Absinthes are not the "real thing." As well, before food laws were introduced in the early 20th century, food ingredients including their sources, amounts, quality, transportation, preparation, and processing were not regulated with producers and sometimes ingredients with toxic or unknown side effects were used. These variances would definitely cause differences in the final product, raising concerns with safety and quality issues. Since food regulations were adopted by the European Union in 1988, low and high quality forms of Absinthe have been discovered. In extreme quantities, thujone exhibits toxic effects and may cause hyperactivity, excitability, delirium, seizures or worse. The probabilities of experiencing these effects are minute due to the removal of thujone during the distillation process. Homemade Absinthe, however, has the potential to reveal these toxic effects. It is possible that thujone content did vary especially when combined with other ingredients. This combination was thought to be responsible for the muse's visionary effects.

Although there are scientific theories regarding the causation of these effects, there is no actual evidence to explain the muse's visionary effects. In many of the arts their use of Absinthe seems to create a very fine line between genius and mental illness. Thujone is thought to trigger unexplainable transformations of the mind and appears to improve sensory perception, cognitive and creative abilities.

The only evidence found to support these transformations is the central nervous system cholinergic receptor binding activity occurring in the brain which scientists claim improves cognitive functions. Absinthe, while the target of many urban legends, did seem to bring out both of the genius and mental illness qualities in a select group of people in the arts. Artists such as Van Gogh, Degas, Gauguin, Mamet, Picasso, and Toulouse-Lautrec; novelists including Oscar Wilde, Ernest Hemingway; musicians such as Liszt; poets, entertainers, and other 'wild men and women' often met the green fairy in local Montmartre cafés. Other non-Parisian fans of the green fairy were Edgar Allan Poe, Jules Verne, Sarah Bernhardt, and Mata Hari. Thujone is an ingredient thought to be responsible for improving cognitive functions, but may also cause a nervous or mental disorder when too much Absinthe is consumed which is known as

Absinthism. This mental disorder was thought to cause hallucinations, mental problems and criminal activity. This is a theory used to explain the reason Van Gogh cut off his ear. Absinthe has also become popular among recent artists and celebrities such as heavy rock singer Marilyn Manson and Johnny Depp being current green fairy fans.

Absinthe has played a role in some very famous works of art. Paintings that were inspired by Absinthe are: 'The Absinthe Drinker', Degas's' 'L'Absinthe', Gauguin's 'Dans Un Café at Arles', Van Gogh's 'Night Café at Arles', and Henri de Toulouse-Lautrec's 'Monsieur Boileau at the Café.' Picasso had one of the last paintings involving Absinthe, as it was banned the next year. Picasso's paintings with Absinthe moved him from his Blue Period to Cubism. Edgar Degas painting, "Absinthe", is now in the permanent collection of the Musée d'Orsay in Paris. This painting depicts a man and woman who are sitting in the center and right side of the picture, a glass with green liquid sits in front of the woman. L'Absinthe represents the increasing social isolation in Paris during its stage of rapid growth. The painting received much criticism and was described as ugly, disgusting, and a blow to morality. The woman in the painting was even described as a whore, and she was merely an actress. Queen Victoria serves as an example of this; she enjoyed Vin Mariani, a medicinal tonic wine that contained cocaine. The green fairy of Absinthe remains noticeably absent from the artwork the drink is said to have inspired. Exceptions can be found in Maignan's 'Green Muse' and Oliva's most famous painting, "the Absinthe Drinker". This piece portrays a man holding his head at an outdoor café while sitting across the table from the green fairy. Arguably, this is meant to depict the love-hate relationship between artistic expansion and madness with the psychoactive and additive effects of Absinthe. It is also interesting to note that Walt Disney's character 'Tinkerbelle', featured in the 1953 film 'Peter Pan', is a green fairy. 'Peter Pan' is based on a James Barrie play from 1904 and the novel 'Peter and Wendy' from 1911. Since Barrie was a devout Calvinist, his involvement with Absinthe seems unlikely, suggesting the connection is mere coincidence. The green muse not only had quite an influence upon the visual arts but many literalists also drank Absinthe while writing, including Edgar Allen Poe, Ernest Hemingway, and Oscar Wilde. As well, Arthur Rimbaud and Paul Verlaine who are also associated with Absinthe and suffered from alcohol intoxication cited the green muse as inspiration. Across the English Channel in England, Oscar Wilde wrote a short eloquent summary about the relationship of his favourite drink Absinthe and life, "Absinthe has a wonderful color, green. A glass of absinthe is as poetical as anything in the world. What difference is there between a glass of absinthe and a sunset? After the first glass you see things as you wish they were. After the second, you see things as they are not. Finally you see things as they really are, and that is the most horrible thing in the world."

Later in 1918, Crowley wrote a lyrical essay in honour of his green fairy entitled "The Green Goddess", a tribute to the high esteem with which he regarded Absinthe. But this ode to the green muse was written in New Orleans not Paris, the Absinthe capital of North America.

And if you think that suggestive advertising is a 20th century phenomenon, try looking at some of the advertising for Absinthe. Some absinthe producers advertised their product with posters of scantily clad women or women in suggestive poses holding up a glass of Absinthe, almost like a libation to the gods. Other posters had a woman dressed like a goddess pointing out a bottle of Absinthe to a bone tired traveler. Regardless of producer, Absinthe was advertised as a pick-me-up which gave energy. But whatever the poster, Absinthe's ability to make a person happy was always shown by happy smiling people usually involved in energetic activities (*cf.* Figure 7, p. 52). Suggestive advertising anyone?

Figure 7
A very popular artistic print which advertised the properties of Vin Mariani at the turn of the 1900s.
Copy of print owned by
Professor M. F. Marcone.

Oscar Wilde's short description of Absinthe may be enough to stay away from it, as it may affect some people with unexpected and disturbing psychological effects. Wilde may not only have been dancing with the green muse when he wrote 'For Whom the Bell Tolls' but he also knew her intimately when he wrote his brief ode to Absinthe. The muse's abilities to induce two seemingly opposite effects at the same time may seem contradictory in our 'age of science, reason, and logic'. While Oscar Wilde may have been entertaining the green muse many times during his deep thoughts, his artistic talent, perception, and his insight about the realities of life are lucid and quite perceptive. Oscar Wilde may have drank to numb the pain he felt from his experiences, although the addiction may prove to be just as inexorable as the pain he felt. Society's obsession with Absinthe was an unrelenting force that reflected the dark times.

Since the late 20th century, the green muse has slowly reappeared, and has become legalized in many countries, although its production and sale is often strictly regulated. Absinthe has once again developed a group of followers. But all is not well for those who want to dance with the seductive and alluring green muse; many who are lured to her believe the myths about

Absinthe but do not read and understand its treacherous history. The words of the Spanish philosopher George Santayana (1863-1952) should be taken to heart: "Those who are ignorant of the past are bound to repeat it."

Figure 8
Photo showing Professor M. F. Marcone with an extremely rare bottle of Vin Mariani dating back to 1895. Using Nuclear Magnetic Resonance (MNR) analysis,
Professor Marcone was able to confirm the composition of the wine without having to open the bottle. Dr. Marcone was able to maintain the value and integrity of this historical and valuable wine.

Glossary

Absinthe: A green liqueur with a high alcohol content and licorice flavour. It is technically a gin, and prepared from the Artemisia absinthium (wormwood) plant, green anise, sweet fennel and other herbs. It is banned in many countries due to its high toxicity. Also known as the Green Fairy or Green Muse. This has been bottled with up to 90% alcohol.

Absinthism: A disorder associated with the habitual abuse of absinthe. It was thought to be the cause behind the hallucinations, tremors and erratic behaviour.

Antimony trichloride: A soft, colourless solid with a pungent odour that was added to imitation Absinthe to increase the louche effect. Chemical formula: $SbCl_3$.

Aperitif: An alcoholic drink with the purpose of stimulating the appetite before a meal.

Artemisia: Any of various aromatic plants of the genus *Artemisia* in the composite family, having green or greyish foliage and usually numerous small discoid flower heads and including the mugwort, sagebrush, tarragon, and wormwood.

Blue period: A period in Picasso's art in which all his works were painted a monotone blue.

Chlorophyll: The green pigment found in plant material responsible for the absorption of photons of light to provide energy for photosynthesis.

Cholinergic receptor: A receptor in the nervous system that responds to the neurotransmitter (A chemical that is passed from one neuron to the next to portray a signal) acetylcholine then carries out a specified action.

Coca: A plant grown in South America (mostly Peru) consumed for thousands of years and is said to have psychoactive effects. The cash crop for production of cocaine.

Congeners: Chemical impurities that change the taste and aroma of distilled alcoholic beverages. It has been suggested that congeners may contribute to the effects of hangover."

Cubism: An abstract art movement of the early 1900s, started by Picasso, which involved arrangement of geometrical shapes.

Devotees: People who are very enthusiastic and committed to something, such as a sport or hobby.

Edgar Degas: A French artist famous for Impressionism (Artwork including small, thin, visible brushstrokes to emphasize light quality change).

Edouard Manet: A 19th century French painter who brought modern-life subjects to his artwork.

Elixir: Sweetened liquid that may contain alcohol that is used for medicinal purposes or as flavouring. Some elixirs are designed to induce drowsiness or sleep.

Eloquent: Having or exercising the power of fluent, forceful, and appropriate speech. Excessive fluidity in knowledge portrayal.

European Union (EU): An economic and political union of 27 countries in Europe that has developed a single market through a standardized system of laws which apply to all members.

Extrait d'absinthe: Translates to "absinthe extract".

Gas Chromatography: The process by which compounds were turned into vapours to separate the individual chemicals for analysis.

Green Muse: see *Absinthe.*

Hallucinations: An experience involving the apparent perceptions of something not present.

Hallucinogenic: A substance which causes hallucinations.

Hydroxyl group: A chemical functional group containing an oxygen atom covalently bound to a hydrogen atom.

Hyperexcitability: A state in which the nerves are unusually easy to excite.

Impurities: Substances within another (liquid, gas or solid), which differ from the chemical composition of the material or compound.

Jolie: Translates to "pretty".

La belle époque: Translates to "beautiful era", a period of time in European history beginning in the late 19th century lasting until WWI.

La Fée Verte: Translates to "the green fairy", referring to absinthe.

La Vie Bohemè: Translates to "bohemian life", a famous French song in the musical "Rent" that celebrates the Bohemian lifestyle.

Louche effect: The gradual change in opaqueness of absinthe when water is added (natural green to a cloudy white).

Maître d': A waiter in a restaurant/dining room providing service to customers.

Morphine: A powerful drug derived from opium. It is used primarily in the management of moderate to severe pain and can also be used as a sedative. It acts on the nervous system to depress nerve impulse transmission, thereby reducing a person's perception of pain. It is a highly addictive drug.

Muse: A source of inspiration; a guiding genius.

Opium: A highly addictive narcotic drug that relieves pain. It is the milky substance produced by the pods of the opium poppy which also contains several other alkaloids, the most important being morphine (from which heroin is derived). It is poisonous in large doses. See *Morphine*.

Oscar Wilde: An Irish writer and poet who was an avid absinthe consumer, often writing about the drink in connection with the creative process.

Pablo Picasso: A Spanish artist most renowned for his abstract painting style.

Paul Gauguin: A French artist specializing in Impressionism.

Prohibition: The Prohibition was the period from 1920 to 1933 when the manufacture, sale, and transportation of intoxicating beverages was outlawed.

Psychoactive: A drug that is capable of influencing mental processes resulting in positive/enjoyable changes in mood, perception, consciousness, cognition and behaviour.

Sage: Any plant or shrub belonging to the genus Salvia, of the mint family.

Tansy: Any of several composite plants of the genus *Tanacetum*, especially a strong-scented, weedy, Old World herb, *T. vulgare*, having flat-topped clusters of tubular yellow flowers.

Temperance movement: A social movement to decrease the consumption of alcohol.

Tetrahydrocannabinol (THC): The principle psychoactive ingredient in the cannabis plant.

The Absinthe Drinker: A famous painting by Viktor Olivia that features absinthe.

Thujone: The main constituent in cedar leaf oil. It has shown to be a stimulant and a convulsant.

Toulouse-Lautrec: A French painter and illustrator.

Tumultuous: Highly agitated, distraught, or turbulent state of mind or emotion.

United States Department of Agriculture (USDA): The department responsible for developing and executing policies regarding farming, agriculture, and food.

Vin (Tonique) Mariani: Bordeaux wine containing cocaine from coca leaves and caffeine from kola nuts.

Vincent Van Gogh: A Deutsch post-impressionist artist who was famous in the 20th century.

Women's emancipation movement: A feminist movement allowing women the right to vote.

References

Absinthe fever. 2006. Thujone. Retrieved from: http://www.absinthefever.com/thujone Alcohol and drug interactions.

Alcohol 101. Retrieved from: http://www.wwu.edu/chw/preventionandwellness/AODWebPDFs/Alcohol&Other DrugInteractions.pdf

Alcohol and Tobacco Tax and Trade Bureau. TTB.gov. Retrieved from: http://www.ttb.gov/index.shtml

Artemisia. 2012. Dictionary.com. Retrieved from: http://dictionary.reference.com/browse/Artemisia?s=t

Basilique du sacre couer. 2012. Wikipedia. Retrieved from: http://en.wikipedia.org/wiki/Basilique_du_Sacré-Cœur,_Paris

Delaney, R. How to drink absinthe. wikiHow. Retrieved from: http://www.wikihow.com/Drink-Absinthe

Eadie, M. J. 2009. Absinthe, epileptic seizures and Valentin Magnan. *Journal of the Royal College of Physicians Edinburgh*, 39, 73-78.

Emmert, J. 2010. Absinthe, Absinthism and Thujone - New Insight into the Spirit's Impact on Public Health. *The Open Addiction Journal*, 3, 32-38.

Fenchone, Pinocamphone, Methanol, Copper, and Antimony Concentrations. *Journal of Agricultural and Food Chemistry*, 56, 3073-3081.

Firedog. Erowid experience vaults: coca & alcohol. Erowid. Retrieved from: http://www.erowid.org/experiences/exp.php?ID=51792

Gas chromatography. Wikipedia. Retrieved from: http://en.wikipedia.org/wiki/Gas_chromatography

Green devil. Absinthe in the US. Retrieved from: http://www.greendevil.com/absinthe_us.html

Holstege, C. P.; Baylor, M. R.; and Rusyniak, D. E. 2002. Absinthe: Return of the Green Fairy. *Seminars in Neurology*, 22(1), 89-93.

Hutton, I. 2002. Myth, Reality and Absinthe. *Current Drug Discovery*, 5, 62-64.

How to Make and Drink Absinthe. Absinthe. Retrieved from:
http://www.originalabsinthe.com/absinthe_faq.php#3

Lachenmeier, D W.; Nathan-Maister, D.;Breaux, T. A.; Luauté, J. P.; and Joachim Emmert.
2010. Absinthe, Absinthism and Thujone – New Insight into the Spirit's Impact on Public
Health. *The Open Addiction Journal*, 3, 32-38.

Lachenmeier, D. W.; Maister, D. N.; Breaux, T. A.; Sohnius, E. M.; Schoeberl, K.; and Kuballa,
T. 2008. Chemical Composition of Vintage Preban Absinthe with Special Reference to
Thujone, Fenchone, Pinocamphone, Methanol, Copper, and Antimony Concentrations. *Journal
of Agricultural and Food Chemistry*, 56(9), 3073-3081.

Lachenmeier, D. W.; and Nathan-Maister, D. 2007. Systematic misinformation about Thujone
in Pre-ban Absinthe. *Deutsche Lebensmittel-Rundschau*, 103(6), 255-263.

Lachenmeier, D. W.; Walch, S .G.; Padosch, S. A.; and Kröner, L. U. 2006. Absinthe - A
Review. Critical Reviews in Food Science and Nutrition, 46, 365-377.

Lee, R. A.; and Balick, M. J. 2005. Absinthe: La Fée Vert. *Ethnomedicine*, 1(3), 217-219.

Medterms. 2004. MedicineNet.com. Retrieved from:
http://www.medterms.com/script/main/art.asp?articlekey=39716

Meschler, J. P.; and Howlett, A. C. 1999. Thujone Exhibits Low Affinity for Cannabinoid
Receptors But Fails to Evoke Cannabimimetic Responses. *Pharmacology Biochemistry and
Behavior,* 62(3), 473-480.

Patočka, J.; and Plucar, B. 2003. Pharmacology and toxicology of absinthe. *Journal of Applied
Biomedicine*, 1, 199-205.

Receptors But Fails to Evoke Cannabimimetic Responses. *Pharmacology Biochemistry and
Behavior*, 62(3), 473-480.

Vogt, D. D.; and Montagne, M. 1982. Absinthe: Behind the Emerald Mask. *The International
Journal of the Addictions*, 17(6), 1015-1029.

Oxygenee's Absinthe History & FAQ IV. Oxygenne Ltd. 2006. Retrieved from:
http://www.oxygenee.com/absintheFAQ4.html

Page, H. 2012. Sacré-coeur: A basilica on the "mount of martyrs". Retrieved from:
http://www.travelsignposts.com/France/sightseeing/basilica-sacre-coeur-paris

Sage. 2012. Dictionary.com. Retrieved from: http://dictionary.reference.com/browse/sage?s=t
Tansy. 2012. The Free Dictionary. Retrieved from: http://www.thefreedictionary.com/tansy
The history of absinthe. Absinthe. Retrieved from: http://www.absinthe.se/absinthe-facts-and-
history/history-of-absinthe

Thujone. Wikipedia. Retrieved from: http://en.wikipedia.org/wiki/Thujone

Thujone and absinthe: mind-bending effects? Absinthe fever: all about the absinthe drink and green fairy lifestyle. Retrieved from: http://www.absinthefever.com/thujone

Thujone definition. Drugs. Retrieved from: http://www.drugs.com/dict/thujone.html

Walsh, Don. 1999. Absinth. http://www.3dchem.com/molecules.asp?ID=142.

Wolff, J. S. 2008. The story of Paris churches. London: C. Palmer & Hayward. Retrieved from:http://www.archive.org/stream/storyofparischur00wolfrich/storyofparischur00wolfrich_djvu.txt

§ 2:

Chocolate …

A New World Aphrodisiac

If there is one food that we can all identify with when we succumb to our guilty pleasure, it's chocolate. Once the exclusive right of Aztec, Mayan, and European royalty and nobility; its presence as a dessert food has made commercial success over the years dating back to 1819, where the first edible piece of chocolate was produced in Switzerland. Cocoa was initially utilized for religious purposes and rituals for ancient Mayan ceremonies to keep the memory of their god, Quetzalcoatl, alive. Upon discovery by Christopher Columbus, this delicacy made its way to Europe in 1502, when Columbus transported the cocoa plant from Mexico to Spain. The immediate widespread popularity led to its mass production and commercialization. Chocolate has become an important part of Western food culture being associated with national holidays such as Easter, Christmas and Hanukkah, Thanksgiving, Valentine's Day, and significant and important family celebrations including engagements, weddings, anniversaries, and birthdays. There is no question that the pleasurable effects of enjoying such a highly palatable food has kept this sweet treat around, moreover, research shows that consumption of chocolate results in psychochemical effects, deeming it an aphrodisiac.

Mankind's desire to have and to use aphrodisiacs, *i.e.* substance that arouses sexual desire and/or enhances sexual performances, is a millennia old quest in both Western and Eastern cultures and traditions. Although the concept of aphrodisiacs are influenced by culture and tradition, the actual word itself is derived from a combination of two words, the name Aphrodite (daughter of Zeus, goddess of sensuality and love, an epitome of beauty, sexual desire, and attraction) and the suffix *–iac* meaning pertaining to, *e.g.* cardiac - relating to the heart. The topic of aphrodisiac is a very controversial one in scientific circles as many argue the effects to be purely placebo in nature. While being a controversial topic, the sexual enhancement industry is booming, making aphrodisiacs a highly marketable item. The main goal for a substance to be an aphrodisiac is that it impacts all or any of the senses, such as sight, touch, smell and taste.

Chocolate is one of the major mainstream aphrodisiacs. Dark chocolate in particular is known due to a molecule it contains. Phenylethylamine (PEA), found in decent concentrations in chocolate is a molecule that stimulates the release of dopamine, a neurotransmitter. Dopamine in particular, is very important in sexual function and gratification. It does so by increasing blood flow in male and female sex organs, improving sexual desire and performance. Another side effect of chocolate is that it helps increase the production of Nitrous oxide which is a powerful vasodilator of blood vessels, increasing blood flow to all parts of the body.

The first group of aphrodisiacs refers to stimulation of the 5 senses (eyes, ears, nose, mouth, skin). Probably the oldest human aphrodisiac is perspiration, *i.e.* sweat which can act as a powerful odorous sexual attractant, a phenomenon observed in animals using pheromones to attract, or sometimes repel, possible sexual mates. A report, published in January 2009 in The Journal of Neuroscience, showed that women were able to distinguish the odour of sexual sweat from regular sweat by processing the odours in different parts of the brain. The women in this study did not distinguish in their verbal responses, the sexual from the neutral sweat, but two regions of the brain responded more to the sexual sweat of men than to any of the other smells.

The second group of aphrodisiacs involves stimuli resulting from the consumption of substances *e.g.* foods, beverages (including alcohol), drugs (including medical preparations), love potions*, etc.* which may have physiological or psychoactive effect based on their active component chemicals. "There are some components of oysters that might promote them as having aphrodisiac qualities. But there is a lot of folkloric myth there," says Aloysa Hourigan, a senior nutritionist with Nutrition Australia. "Results generally support the hypothesis that red induces higher arousal levels than green. The effect on absolute conductance level was small, but there was a clear difference in rapid conductance changes (GSRs) to the onset of the stimuli. Subjective reports were consistent with the electrodermal evidence; the red was variously described as more stimulating, exciting, awakening, attention-drawing, overpowering, and lively."

The third group of aphrodisiacs are animal products, such as rhinoceros horn, tiger penis, and stag antlers whose aphrodisiac effect is a combination of externally generated stimuli, consumption, and traditional belief system. Objects such as these are visually phallic in nature but have traditionally been incorporated in orally consumed treatments used to treat a variety of physical sexual dysfunctions. This notion stems from the belief that "God designated his purpose for things by their appearance". As such, those that consume a particular product would retain the properties and/or characteristics of the item consumed. No scientific identifiable and/or verifiable substances, however, have been identified in any of these three items, or in any similar items, which can be considered to have aphrodisiac effects. In fact, pharmaceutical company, Hoffman-La Roche, conducted a series of tests on the Rhinoceros horn to confirm these findings. They found that consumption of rhino horn had no effect on the human body, whether good or bad. These ancient traditional uses coupled with habitat loss have caused many of these animals to become endangered or be put on the Endangered Species List with the result that any trade, global, national, or local, or use of any of their 'products' is not only illegal but also considered immoral by countries who have signed these treatises.

Many world governments have increased regulations and laws to protect consumers from unregistered and false substances within food and drug products. In 1989, the US FDA declared, based on scientific analysis and safety, that there is no evidence that over-the-counter aphrodisiacs treat sexual dysfunction. The declaration was intended to warn and protect consumers from unregulated and potentially dangerous over-the-counter 'aphrodisiac' substances such as Spanish Fly which is powdered *Lytta vesicatoria*, an emerald green blister beetle. This 'product' can contain a toxic substance called cantharidin, which is poisonous and has an LD50 (lethal dose of a toxic substance which is fatal to 50% of a tested population after a specific time period) of 0.5 mg/kg, with10 mg being potentially fatal. Upon ingestion, cantharidin can cause genital inflammation, enhancing genital nerve sensation and thus acting as an aphrodisiac. "Aphrodisiac products" such as Spanish Fly, however, are commonly viewed negatively due to their alluring and profitable nature. As well, there are many similar concerns for other products sold over-the-counter that also contain unregulated and potentially dangerous substances. While many ancient writings purport the existence of aphrodisiacs, one may wonder if there are any modern day aphrodisiacs. In March 1998, the US Food and Drug Administration (US FDA) approved the drug Sildenafil (*aka* Viagra); the first legally approved treatment that could be taken by mouth for male erectile dysfunction. While the US FDA may not regard Viagra as an aphrodisiac, our definition of an aphrodisiac (substances which increase sexual arousal, increase sexual potency, and/or enhance sexual pleasure) would put Viagra and other similar man-made drugs sold in pharmacies in this category. Although it is a man-made (as opposed to natural) drug, Viagra was initially developed to treat pulmonary hypertension and altitude pulmonary edema. This is because in addition to regulating blood flow to the penis, Viagra relaxes the pulmonary arterial wall in the heart, decreasing the arterial pressure build up that is characteristic of pulmonary hypertension. This relaxation consequently offloads the right ventricle and makes it easier for oxygen to be pumped through the body system thereby helping with altitude pulmonary edema. Its sales in the United States and elsewhere (including competitors Cialis and

Levitra), has skyrocketed to say the least. The emergence of Viagra has mirrored the public response to the work of Masters and Johnson who were among the first to study and publish findings on sexual responses in humans from 1957 into the 1990s. Both have highlighted issues related to human sexuality, its expression, and its enjoyment.

To the delight of chocolate lovers, chocolate is believed to possess among the strongest aphrodisiac effects in the world. In both the Mayan and Aztec cultures, chocolate is offered in various forms to the gods, but more importantly to the gods of creation and fertility. Each spring the Aztec emperor dug the first furrow in the spring to represent his union with the fertility goddess to guarantee a rich harvest because these cultures believed that the fertility of their king was directly related to the fertility of the land. In ancient Mayan and Aztec cultures, chocolate was prepared from crushed cocoa beans whipped with hot water into foam. Being quite bitter, the Mayans added chilies which improved its taste as well as increased the 'heat' from the capsaicin in the chilies. The kings drank large amounts of this form of chocolate on a daily basis. Aztec emperor Maltezuma is allegedly supposed to drink 50 chocolate drinks each day, especially at night before engaging in sexual activity. This association of chocolate with sexual activity, the burning effect contributed by the chilies, along with the myths of creation and fertility in certain cultures all contributed to these beliefs of aphrodisiac in chocolate.

The word "chocolate" is a New World word with Mesoamerican origin and heritage, although its etymology is still much debated. One theory is that it originates from 'xocolātl' (pronounced 'sho-co-la-tl'), a Mesoamerican word meaning 'bitter water', which describes their cocoa-based beverage. This beverage was made of water, chili peppers, cornmeal and cocoa, of course cocoa (Kerr). The inhabitants of this area were thought to have started consuming this liquid as early as 1900-1500 B.C.E. The clearest instance of usage of cacao, however, is in the

Mayan culture in 250-900 A.D. Not only was cocoa made into delicious drinks to be consumed, especially by those of higher class, it also served as a sacred tool on religious occasions. Cocoa was introduced to European society by the Spanish explorers in the early 1500s; within 100 years it had spread throughout Europe, being used as both medicinal and culinary ingredients. Chocolate became a much-desired product and remained a symbol of high standing in society. Cacao seeds (*aka* beans) are derived from the fruit of a 4-8 meter tall tree called *Theobroma cacao, i.e.* 'food/drink of the gods'. While the plant has debatable Mesoamerican origins, current genetic studies place its beginnings in the Amazon basin. This evergreen tree with poisonous and inedible leaves prefers to grow in the shade of taller trees, requiring the warm, moist and humid climates with fertile tropical soils. These specific growing conditions are only found in a narrow band around the equator, bounded on the north by the Tropic of Cancer and on the south by the Tropic of Capricorn. This geographical area embraces the world's cocoa producing countries in Africa, South America, Mexico, Indonesia, Papua New Guinea, Malaysia, Togo, India, the Philippines and the Solomon Islands.

The tree, *Theobroma cacao*, fruits three to four times each year. Oval shaped pods (like a football) grow from the tree directly from the tree trunk or large branches instead of at the end of branches like most plants or trees. The pods start out green during their development and when ripe they change colour. They transition to yellow, orange, red or purple when ripe, although some pods stay green even when ripe. They generally weigh one pound and their length can vary from 10cm to 40cm and more. These one pound cacao pods are harvested by hands. It requires one to identify the mature pods and cut them from the tree. The pods are then cautiously broken in half. Inside the pods are cacao seeds (each pod contains about 20-60 seeds, which have about 40% fat). These seeds are embedded within a white pulp. After removal from the pods, the cacao seeds are fermented, dried, cleaned, and roasted.

Once the seeds and pulp are then taken out of the pod, they are put into piles on mats or banana leaves. They are then covered or put into a bin or box with a lid. Fermentation results because the sugars in the pulp are converted into alcohol by yeast. Afterwards, the beans are mixed carefully to bring oxygen into the mix and this converts the alcohol into lactic and acetic acid. Now, the cacao pods are referred to as cocoa beans. At this point the cocoa beans have high moisture content and to change this quality, they must be dried. The drying process is different at different plantations according to two variables. It is contingent on the climate or size of the plantation. Cocoa beans can be dried out in the sun on trays or mats where the climate is dry enough. As well, this method of sun-drying usually happens in smaller plantations. Daily rainfall occurs often in tropical areas thus the beans cannot be sundried. Alternatively, the beans can be dried in sheds on the condition that there is sufficient air flowing around the beans in the shed. It is best to let regular air dry the beans. This is because alternative methods lead to disliked results. For example, making a fire with wood and using the heat from this fire to accelerate the drying process is disliked by bulk chocolate manufacturers, chocolatiers and consumers, as this process gives the beans a smoky taste.

When the cocoa beans have dried out enough so that the moisture percentage in the cocoa beans is 6-7 percent, the beans are sorted and bagged. It is essential that the beans are sorted because within the industry cocoa beans are categorized and sold by their size and quality. The cocoa beans are packaged and shipped to chocolate manufactures. At the manufacturing plants the cocoa beans go through a sampling, testing and cleaning procedure. Sample cocoa beans are tested for size and flaws such as insects and mold. As well the sample beans are turned into chocolate liquor and the liquor is tasted by company tasters to be assessed for flavour and aroma. Additionally, the beans are carefully cleaned to get rid of any foreign matter.

The beans are then put into a roaster. As the bean is roasted, its shell splits from the bean kernel because the shell becomes dry and lightweight as a result of the roasting. The inner part of the cocoa bean or soft tissue of the cocoa bean is then broken into smaller pieces as they pass through serrated (jagged) cones. It is important to note that the beans are not crushed during this process they are just split into smaller pieces and are now referred to as cocoa nibs. The nibs are grounded or crushed in a milling or grinding machine such as a melangeur to convert the nibs into a thick liquid called chocolate liquor. The chocolate liquor does not contain alcohol, the purpose of the name is to communicate that it is in liquid form. Further processing occurs, where the chocolate liquor is pressed to remove the cocoa butter. This process leaves behind a solid mass that is crushed into cocoa powder (also called cocoa solids). The cocoa butter and cocoa solids are blended together but in different quantities with more ingredients such as sugar, milk powder and other ingredients that enhance flavouring. For example, milk chocolate contains sugar, milk or milk powder, cocoa solids (also known as cocoa powder), cocoa liquor, cocoa butter, lecithin (an emulsifier) and vanilla. Overall, the amount of cocoa butter, cocoa solids, milk and other ingredients used in making chocolate is contingent on the type of chocolate being made (*e.g.* dark, white, milk). Beginning in the 1500s, the Aztecs traded with the Mayans and others for cacao. At one point cacao seeds were used as a form of Aztec money. Following this in 1519, Hernando Cortez created a plantation in an attempt to "grow" money.

After its conquest of the Aztec Empire in the 1500s, the Spanish brought the novel but bitter Mesoamerican chocolate beverage to the Spanish court, its popularity as both a medicinal and culinary ingredient eventually spreading into the rest of Western Europe in less than 100 years. But this unsweetened beverage from the New World was consumed only by kings and nobles alike as it was too expensive for the everyday poor labourer. The first chocolate house opened in London in 1657 and acted much like the recently opened European coffee houses, a place to discuss the day's business and other topics of current global and local importance.

The subsequent history of chocolate is filled with many familiar names of well-known companies producing chocolate who have delighted 'chocoholics' around the world. Hans Sloane (1660-1753), a physician living in Jamaica, invented the first sweetened milk chocolate beverage as a medicinal drink, much like the forerunner of Coca Cola™ a few centuries later. In 1897, this formula was sold to the Cadbury brothers, and the rest is history. The first solid form of chocolate was developed by Joseph Fry & Sons in 1847 who invented a novel processing method of separating and recombining cocoa solids and cocoa butter with other ingredients such as sugar moulding the paste into a bar. Three decades later in 1879, Henri Nestlé (1814-1890), a German confectioner collaborated with Daniel Peter (1836-1919), a Swiss chocolatier, to create the first milk chocolate bar. In the same year, Rudolphe Lindt (1855-1909) invented conching, a refining step in the chocolate making process which ensured a consistent shiny and non-gritty chocolate with a silky smooth and creamy texture. American confectioner and philanthropist, Milton Hershey (1857-1945) was the first person to mass produce chocolate, lowering the per-unit cost of making milk chocolate bars affordable for everyone. It was Hersey's continual dedication to chocolate research and innovation which enabled US troops to have chocolate that did not melt, a valuable and popular item which affectionately became known as Field ration D.

Many people and companies in the chocolate business have contributed much to the development of chocolate as well as technological innovations in chocolate manufacture. Many current companies have not publically admitted to performing research into the aphrodisiac properties of chocolate. The chocolate industry is a 50 billion dollar company that is still growing each year. While a positive finding would boost their sales, a negative finding would equally cause fewer chocolate sales, and hence lower profits.

Always a topic of immense interest is the discussion involving the psychoactive effects of aphrodisiacs, a discussion which is often a mixture of both fact and urban myths. According to ancient texts, some foods produce aphrodisiac effects when consumed. To be considered effective aphrodisiacs, however, substances in these foods must be able to cross the blood barrier found in the human brain, in acceptable amounts, which directly/indirectly stimulate areas of the brain involved in sexual arousal as well as the presence of sufficient numbers of appropriate receptors in the tissues/organs involved in human sexual arousal, performance, vigour, and/or fertility.

Chocolate contains many different chemicals which are thought to either directly or indirectly influence both mood as well as sexual behaviour. One such ingredient is its antioxidants, naturally occurring chemicals also found in foods and beverages such as wine, green tea, coffee, fruits, vegetables, and whole grains. Antioxidants protect cells in the body against unstable oxygen compounds (free radicals) produced as part of natural metabolism. Normal levels of free radicals can be controlled, however factors such as tobacco smoke, environmental toxins and radiation can lead to increased production of free radicals; free radical accumulation can lead to cell damage and impair normal cell function. These free radicals set in motion a cascade, which is believed to be a contributor to the aging process as well many diseases. In chocolate, these flavonoid antioxidants (polyphenols) are found mostly in the cocoa solids. The highest amounts are found in dark chocolate which contains the most cocoa solids; dark chocolate with 71% cocoa has 4x the amount of flavonoids than red wine. Flavonoid content is variable as growing conditions, variety, fermentation, roasting, and other processing methods can decrease the content. It has also been suggested that antioxidant capacity and flavonoid plasma content are reduced if the dark chocolate is consumed with milk or if milk is incorporated into the product (*i.e.* Milk chocolate). They found that two times the amount of milk chocolate would need to be consumed in order to match the antioxidant capacity from a similar serving size of dark chocolate. In terms of drinking milk at the same time as eating dark chocolate, the antioxidant capacity was greatly inhibited as bonds were formed between the milk proteins and the flavonoids, making it less accessible to the cell. In one clinical investigation, Dr. Alan Hirsch, neurological director of The Smell and Taste Treatment and Research Center foundation in Chicago conducted research on the effect of blood to the penis as a result of either eating dark chocolate (highest in antioxidant flavonoids) and/or inhaled chocolate aroma. This increased flow was measured through a customized "blood pressure" cuff which was put around the base of the penis before experimentation. The results showed that both the consumption of the dark chocolate as well as the inhaled chocolate aroma increased blood flow to the penis as indicated by an increase in blood pressure. This shows that chocolate has a particular and distinct ingredient that enrichness and enhances blood flow to the male penis. Increased penile blood flow is the first physical sign of sexual excitation. As the concentration of flavonoids increase and/or the chocolate scent increased, so did the rise in penile pressure indicating that both consumption and inhalation had a definite dose-response relationship! The investigators theorized that the antioxidants or flavonoids in the consumed dark chocolate had a direct effect in increasing the amount of nitric oxide production which increased both blood to and pressure in the penis, both events critical for an erection. Antioxidants, however, include a number of enzymes and other substances such as vitamin C which have been shown to possibly reduce the risks of cancer and age-related macular degeneration. Also, the beneficial effects of flavonoids are presented as treatment of bruises, contusions, and sprains. All in all both these combination increased both blood to and pressure in the penis, both events critical for an erection.

The same effects as seen in the inhaled chocolate aroma, however, are not clearly understood except that the compound(s) responsible must be volatile in sufficient concentrations. Therefore, the compounds responsible are able to transform into gases at room temperature, and then the gases are inhaled. Regardless of effect, perhaps both men and women need to have some good quality dark chocolates in the night table next to their beds. Not only does chocolate have compounds, which are beneficial; for the heart and circulatory system, it also contains psychoactive chemicals which can influence mood. Chocolate has been associated with happiness and improved mood due to the psychoactive chemicals found within it. It contains compounds which are beneficial to both the heart and circulatory system. Two main chemicals known to have psychoactive effects include theobromine and caffeine. Both theobromine and caffeine are stimulants, or substances which increase levels of physiological or nervous activity in the body, commonly found in chocolate, tea, and coffee. Theobromine is a smooth muscle stimulant derived from the cacao tree. It is made up of the Greek words; *theo-*god and *brosi-*food, together meaning "food of the gods". Caffeine is a central nervous system stimulant commonly found in tea and coffee products. These compounds have been found to increase alertness, stimulation, and improve reaction time. Another study conducted by Mumford *et al.* showed the combination of caffeine (19 mg) and theobromine (250 mg) increased "energetic arousal" and improved cognitive function. Although both stimulants had psychoactive effects on individuals, researchers found theobromine had only one fifth the potency of caffeine on receptors suggesting it has a significantly lower stimulative effect than caffeine. Theobromine occurs in chocolate at concentrations from 2%-10%, whereas caffeine is only present at concentrations less than 1%. This supports the theory that the stimulatory effects are primarily due to theobromine. Both chemicals produce their stimulatory effects by acting upon the adrenal glands. The adrenal glands are endocrine glands that sit atop the kidney, responsible for releasing hormones in response to stress. The stimulated adrenal gland releases the hormones norepinephrine and epinephrine. These hormones act as neurotransmitters, which are chemicals capable of transmitting neuron signals to a target cell. The neurotransmitters bind to adrenergic receptors on various cells of organ systems, which induce a response in that cell. These receptors are located on many types of cells and when activated, induce the "fight or flight response" that involves increased alertness and wakefulness. This fight or flight response involves increased heart rate, increased blood flow to skeletal muscles, glucose release, bronchodilation, blood vessel contraction, decrease motility of gastrointestinal tract, *etc.*

Furthermore, the amino acid phenylalanine can be broken down to produce phenylethylamine (PEA) *aka* the 'love drug'. PEA mediates the feelings of attraction, excitement, giddiness, apprehension and euphoria. This state of mind stimulates the hypothalamus gland located in the brain to induce pleasurable sensations, as well as affecting the levels of serotonin (mood enhancer and impulse regulator) and endorphins (endo-within, orphin-opiate-like, therefore opiate-like chemicals produced within the body) from the pituitary gland located at the back of the brain. These natural chemicals are released into the nervous system during situations of happiness, feelings of love, passion and lust. Their presence also increases blood pressure, heart rate, glucose levels in the blood and feelings of well-being bordering on euphoria, sensations usually associated with being in love. These effects may be partially responsible for giving chocolate its food aphrodisiac status. Like amphetamines, (a type of CNS stimulant which increases dopamine and norepinephrine levels in the brain inducing euphoria as well as wakefulness and focus) PEA is believed to act as a neurotransmitter stimulating the release of norepinephrine and dopamine (increases heart rate and blood pressure, increases sexual gratification/pleasurable sensations by suppressing the production of prolactin).

Chocolate is known to promote the feeling of euphoria and act as an aphrodisiac in individuals as it contains two fat soluble chemicals, N-acylethanolamines and anandamide. N-acylethanolamines is a fatty acid derivative and is structurally similar to anandamides. After ingestion, N-acylethanolamine circulates throughout the body and, when present in the brain prevents the degradation of anandamides. N-acylethanolamine is also able to bind cannabinoid, peroxisome proliferator activated and vanilloid receptors. The psychoactive compound in marijuana (THC) also binds cannabinoid receptors which are of particular importance. These are present in the cell membranes of neurons in the brain and suppress the release of the neurotransmitter GABA while promoting the release of serotonin. This combines to act as an anti-depressant leading to the feeling of euphoria as well as acting as an appetite promoter. THC reduces REM sleep and memory capability while increasing the occurrences of panic reactions and delusions. These negative effects of THC are not observed due to N-acylethanolamine.

Chocolate also contains anandamide, a fat-soluble protein that is naturally found in the brain. Anandamide is synthesized in areas of the brain that are important in memory and higher-thought processes. It has a three-dimensional structure, similar to tetrahydrocannabinol (THC), a chemical found in marijuana. It acts as a signalling molecule, binding to cannabinoid receptors and producing similar psychoactive effects of cannabinoid drugs such as heightened sensitivity and euphoria. There are two main types of cannabinoid receptors; the CB1 receptors are found in regions of the brain and other organs like the heart while CB2 receptors are located in leukocytes, spleen and tonsils and modulate immune response. Anandamide may alter the functioning of other neurochemicals such as norepinephrine, dopamine and serotonin. It may also interact with other biologically active constituents of chocolate to induce a sense of well-being.

Anandamide has a short half-life of approximately 5-10 minutes. It is broken down by fatty-acid amide hydrolase (FAAH). It has been speculated that some chocolate N-acylethanolamines may prevent the breakdown of anandaminde leading to a greater than normal accumulation in the brain and thus extending the feeling of euphoria. Studies have shown that inhibition of FAAH activity leads to elevated anandamide levels, increases stress-coping behaviours and increases the firing of serotonergic and noradrenergic neurons in the midbrain.

The psychopharmalogic constituent concentrations in chocolate are so low that they are unlikely to have a significant psychoactive effect. Christian Felder (National Institute of Mental Health) estimates that an average person would have to consume approximately 25 pounds of chocolate all at once to experience any marijuana-like effect. But as with caffeine and most drugs, some people metabolize these chemicals much more slowly and there is no way to predict an amount that would have the same effect in all people.

Chocolate contains over 500 natural chemicals. Since it contains many natural chemicals, chocolate is considered an aphrodisiac. An aphrodisiac is considered a substance that heightens sexual arousal and desire. Improved heart health and increased production of nitric oxide as well as psychoactive effects (effect on mood or behaviour) all contribute to the enjoyment of sexual activity. Flavonoid, which are found in dark chocolates are responsible for the production of nitric oxide, which cause the blood vessels in your body to widen and relax. Different cocoa varieties, processing conditions, and storage environments unfortunately decrease the amount of these chemicals in cocoa solids. Dark and bitter-sweet chocolates are said to have the highest amount of cocoa solids, leading to more antioxidants and psychoactive ingredients. Compared to white chocolate, dark chocolate has the effect of the action of flavonoids which are rich in the natural compounds found in its cocoa beans. As one gets older it is said that it lowers blood pressure, to those who already have mild blood pressure. Milk chocolates, however, contain lesser amounts of cocoa solids, and have more sugar, artificial fats, and taste enhancers. So, what is the bottom line? In a nutshell then, remember that "stressed" spelled backwards is "desserts", think delicious and calming thoughts while reaching for a piece of bitter-sweet or dark chocolate. For aphrodisiac effects, however, you get the greatest bang for your buck (no pun intended) from eating good quality bitter-sweet or dark chocolate in small amounts on a regular basis, sharing and enjoying the experience, pleasure, and benefits, with your loved one.

Glossary

Antioxidants: Any substance that inhibits oxidation.

Amphetamines: a stimulant drug which stimulates the central nervous system and is used primarily to lift the mood in depressive states or to control the appetite in cases of obesity.

Aphrodisiac: An aphrodisiac food, drug, potion, or other agent that arouses sexual desire.

Caffeine : A bitter white alkaloid, $C_8H_{10}N_4O_2$, often derived from tea or coffee and used in medicine chiefly as a mild stimulant and to treat certain kinds of headache.

Central nervous system: The mass of nerve tissue that controls and coordinates the activities of an animal.

Conductance: A measure of a material's ability to conduct electric charge; the reciprocal of the resistance.

Dopamine: A chemical found in the brain that acts as a neurotransmitter and is an intermediate compound in the synthesis of noradrenaline which helps regulate movement and emotion.
Edema: An accumulation of an excessive amount of watery fluid in cells, tissues, or serous cavities.

Electrodermal: Of or relating to the electrical properties of the skin.

Enzyme: Any of numerous proteins or conjugated proteins produced by living organisms and functioning as biochemical catalysts.

Fermentation: The breakdown of sugar into an acid or alcohol.

Flavonoid: Any of a group of organic compounds that occur as pigments in fruit and flowers.

Free Radicals: Are atoms or groups of atoms with an odd (unpaired) number of electrons and can be formed when oxygen interacts with certain molecules.

GABA: A neurotransmitter in the central nervous system that inhibits excitatory responses.

Glucose: Monosaccharide sugar used as the preferred body fuel.

Half-life: The time required for the activity of a substance, taken into the body, to lose half of its initial effectiveness.

Inflammation: A localized protective reaction of tissue to irritation, injury, or infection, characterized by pain, redness, swelling, and sometimes loss of function.

Macular degeneration: A condition in which the cells of the macula lutea degenerate, resulting in blurred vision and ultimately blindness.

Metabolism: The set of chemical reactions that happen in the cells of living organisms to sustain life.

Neurochemicals: A drug or other substance that affects the nervous system.

Neurotransmitter: A chemical by which a nerve cell communicates with another nerve cell or with a muscle.

Norepinephrine: A substance, both a hormone and neurotransmitter, secreted by the adrenal medulla and the nerve endings of the sympathetic nervous system to cause vasoconstriction and increases in heart rate, blood pressure, and the sugar level of the blood.

Phenylethylamine: An amine that occurs naturally as a neurotransmitter in the brain, has proper ties similar to those of amphetamine, is an antidepressant, and is found in chocolate.

Pheromones: A secreted hormone that triggers a social response in members of the same species.

Placebo- A substance having no pharmacological effect which is administered as a control in testing experimentally or clinically to show the efficacy of a biologically active preparation.

Pod: A common name for a simple dry fruit that develops from a simple carpel and usually dehisces (opens along a seam) on two sides.

Polyphenol: Any of various alcohols containing two or more benzene rings that each has at least one hydroxyl group (OH) attached.

Prolactin: A hormone released by the pituitary gland that stimulates breast development and milk production in women.

Psychoactive: Affecting the mind or mental processes.

Psychochemical: Pertaining to chemicals or drugs that affect the mind or behaviour.

Psychopharmacologic: The scientific study of the actions of drugs and their effects on mood, sensation, thinking, and behaviour.

Pulmonary hypertension: This is abnormally high blood pressure in the arteries of the lungs which makes the right side of the heart work harder.

Receptors: A molecule often found on the surface of a cell, which receives chemical signals originating externally from the cell. Through binding to a receptor, these signals direct the cell's actions.

Serotonin: A compound present in blood platelets and serum that constricts the blood vessels and acts as a neurotransmitter.

Stimulant: An agent, especially a chemical agent such as caffeine that temporarily arouses or accelerates physiological or organic activity.

Theobromine: A bitter, colorless alkaloid, $C_7H_8N_4O_2$, derived from the cacao bean, found in chocolate products and used in medicine as a diuretic, vasodilator, and myocardial stimulant.

Vasodilator: A drug, agent, or nerve that can cause dilatation (vasodilatation) of the walls of blood vessels.

References

Afoakwa, E .O. 2008. Cocoa and chocolate consumption - Are there aphrodisiac and other benefits for human health? *South African Journal of Clinical Nutrition*, 21(3), 107-113.

Carlini, E. 2004. The good and the bad effects of (-) trans-delta-9-tetrahydrocannabinol (Delta 9-THC) on humans. *International Society on Toxinology,* 44(4), 461-467.

Cota-Larson, R.; Pappin, S. 2010. Rhino horn: What's the story behind one of the most recognizable features in the animal kingdom? Retrieved from http://rhinoconservation.org/2010/02/21/rhino-horn-knowledge-vs-superstition

Coulon D., Faure L.; Salmon, M.; Wattelet, V; and Bessoule, J. 2012. N-Acylethanolamines and related compounds: aspects of metabolism and functions. *Plant Science,* 184, 129-140.

Denoon, D. J. 2003. WebMD Health News. Retrieved from http://www.webmd.com/diet/news/20030827/dark-chocolate-is-healthy-chocolate.

Differential contributions of theobromine and caffeine on mood, psychomotor performance and blood pressure. *Physiology & Behaviour,* 104, 816-822.

Edmonds, M. 2011. The Myth of Rhino Horn. Retrieved from http://science.discovery.com/top-ten/2009/aphrodisiacs/aphrodisiacs-05.html

Grivetti, L. E. 2007. From Aphrodisiac to Health Food: A Cultural History of Chocolate. Available online : www.karger.com.

Hirsch, A. R. 1998. Smell: The Secret Seducer. *Journal of the American Medical Association,* 279(22), 1840.

Hirsch, A. R. 1996. Use of deodorants to treat male impotence, and article of manufacture therefore. United States Patent, Application number 08/606,544.

Mitchell, E. S.; Slettenaar, M.; Meer, N.; Transler, C.; Jans, L.; Quadt, F.; and Berry, M. 2011. Differential contributions of theobromine and caffeine on mood, psychomotor performance and blood pressure. *Physiology & Behavior*, 104(5), 816-822.

Mumford, K G.; Evans, M .S.; Kaminski, J. B.; Preston, L. K.; Sannerud, A. C.; Silverman, Kenneth; Griffiths, Roland R. 1994. Discriminative stimulus and subjective effects of theobromine and caffeine in humans. *Psychopharmacology*, 115(1-2), 1-8.

Schierenbeck, T.; Riemann, D.; Berger, M; and Hornyak, M. 2008. Effect of illicit recreational drugs upon sleep: cocaine, ecstasy and marijuana. *Sleep Medicine Reviews,* 5, 381-389.

Sandroni, P. 2001. Aphrodisiacs past and present: a historical review. *Clinical Autonomic Research*, 11, 303-307.

Shamloul, R. 2010. Natural Aphrodisiacs. *Journal of Sexual Medicine*, 7, 39-49.

di Tomaso, E.; Beltramo, M.; and Piomelli, D. 1996. Brain cannabionoids in chocolate. *Nature,* 382, 677-678.

Wang, J.; and Ueda. N. 2009. Biology of endocannabinoid synthesis system. *Prostaglandins & other Lipid Mediators*, 89, 112-119.

Taren, D. and Bruinsma, K. 1999. Chocolate, Food or Drug? *Journal of the Academy of Nutrition and Dietetics,* 99(10), 1249-1256.

The Healthy Benefits of Dark Chocolate. 2007. CTV Canada AM. *Bell Media.* Retrieved from http://www.ctv.ca/CTVNews/CanadaAM/20070704/dark_chocolate_070704/

Wasik, A.; Christensson, B.; and Sander, B. 2011. The role of cannabinoid receptors and the endocannabinoid system in mantle cell lymphonma and other non-Hodgkin lymphomas. *Seminars in Cancer Biology*, 5, 313-321.

Zouma, B. L.; Kreiser, W. R.; and Martin, R. 1980. Theobromine and Caffeine Content in Chocolate Products. *Journal of Food Science,* 45, 314-316.

§ 3:

Chili Peppers

Getting a high from life, lunch, and dinner too!

As you are exiting the movie theatre after watching the premiere of a much anticipated movie with your friends, you summarize your impression of the movie, "Wasn't that a fantastic movie?" Everyone agrees that it was such a cool movie so much so that they would like to see it again! Looking at your watch, you notice that it is still early. Having been so engrossed in the movie, your stomach is growling, seemingly making insulting remarks that you have not fed it for a while. "It's still early, how about something to eat?" "Hey, that's a great idea, any suggestions? What are you in the mood for?" Having no clue except that you are hungry, you ask your friends for advice. "How about trying that new restaurant called Tongues on Fire?" Everyone gets into the car and eagerly anticipates talking about the movie over some good spicy food. Not being accustomed to it though, you are a little apprehensive but decide to keep an open mind and, more importantly, an open stomach.

The restaurant is just as you had imagined it; inviting and hospitable, vibrant and colourful, cozy and amenable to conversation. Looking at the menu, you have absolutely no idea of what to order, leaving that decision to your friends as you have decided to share several plates. After ordering both food and drinks, the conversation turns to the movie. The food seems to arrive in no time; as you are excitedly caught up in conversation, you do not notice the passage of time. Everyone begins to partake and starting with the least spicy, you take a few morsels. "Whoo wee, that's spicy, my tongue is on fire!" Your mouth is burning, and everyone is laughing with you as they too are feeling the heat! But despite being initially uncomfortable, you cannot help but eat more as it is so addictive! "Here, eat some of this, it will help." One of your friends has just given you some full-fat sweetened yogurt that really does take the sting out of it. "I must have more of this spicy food. "Mmm, delicious!" Before you know it, hours have passed with invigorating conversation and food but the restaurant is making closing noises; the evening has come to a robust end. "We simply have to do this again. How about next week? I will call everyone and we can decide on another movie, and of course, we will have to come back here again." Everyone agrees while walking to the car eagerly anticipating next week. Arriving home, you bid everyone a final goodnight while affirming the movie and dinner date for next week ... already you are jumping out of your skin with anticipation.

So, what was in that spicy meal which stimulated not only the conversation but also the senses? Ah, it was the humble chili pepper, the second most popular spice in the world after salt. Being the source of much pain, and pleasure, how ironic it is that something so 'toxic' to the taste buds can be so appealing to chili aficionados *aka* 'chili heads'. These 'chili heads' like to 'mouth surf' by challenging their taste buds; getting a natural, and legal, 'high'. Indeed, without being a sadomasochist with all its connotations, there is indeed much pleasure in the pain. Every day, millions of people crave and eagerly consume these fiery peppers, which are a must in the cuisines of many tropical and sub-tropical countries. Not only do they add zest to food but they also add hot passion to life itself! These scorching bundles of heat, distant relatives of other New World vegetables such as potatoes or tomatoes, are members of the Genus *Capsicum* (Latin '*capsa*' meaning hat); a family with 22 wild pepper species with 5 being domesticated by man. The chili pepper is a New World treasure, cultivated by the peoples of both Central and South America for well over 6000 years, with traces being found in Peruvian burial places.

The Pepper's Origin

When Christopher Columbus headed west across the Atlantic Ocean in the late 1400s in search of a short fast route to mysterious, elusive China, he observed that most of Europe did not have many spices that could add flavour and 'heat' to their foods. The only exception was black pepper from India. A physician accompanying Christopher Columbus brought the chili pepper back to Spain where it was called "*pimiento*" meaning 'pepper', probably an allusion to the 'heat' experienced when eating black pepper (*Pipernigrum*). The Latin name for black pepper probably originated from the Sanskirt '*pippali*', a word whose etymology can be traced in many European and Western Asia Semitic languages in nouns and adjectives such as paprika, peppermint, chili, Jamaica pepper (allspice), pepper root (horseradish and ginger) and pepper herb (savoury). With Portugal also having discovered this spice to delight the senses from their explorations in South America, it became an almost instant sensation in both European kitchens and medical practice, being grown in Italy as early as 1526. As the chili pepper thrives in the climates of most southern European countries including the Balkan Peninsula and Northern Africa, this fruit quickly became a popular item in European market places, being used as both a flavouring agent as well as a food preservative. For some unknown reasons, it neither travelled very far beyond these warm areas nor did it seem to be part of most Northern European cuisines. During the rebirth of Europe *aka* the Renaissance (1300s-1600s), Europe experienced a shift in its attitude towards food. Helping to swing the shift in food habits and preferences, ships arrived daily in the sea ports loaded to the top and overflowing with aromatic spices and foods from mysterious far off lands. Their arrival was announced by sea breezes that carried the aroma to land, causing excitement and eager anticipation in these trade ports. Before this age of rebirth and renewal it was believed that one should not take pleasure in food as it was considered sinful, or at least there was a strong temptation to fall into the sin of gluttony. The chili pepper might have found a home in this type of thinking with its 'burning' effect being acceptable but the pleasure aspect would definitely not have been an added benefit, but rather a definite taboo!

The red hot chili from the New World helped the shift to the new hedonistic food pleasure as food was now regarded as a delight to be enjoyed and celebrated in its fullness. Food itself was a gift from God who had created all things, and when He spoke He had pronounced all His created things as being 'good'. Along with many spices from the world over chilis gave a much needed proverbial 'kick' to the tired Old World cuisine, and a whole new and hot personality emerged! In less than 100 years the chili pepper travelled quickly, being brought half way around the world to India and South Asia by Spanish and Portuguese traders where it quickly became a prominent and important food spice and medicinal ingredient. The chili pepper was especially favoured by the Victorians during the 18th century as Indian dishes were very popular during the height of the British Empire in India. In the late 20th century, chlli peppers' 'hotness' as well as that of other spices became popular in countries with more temperate climates as people from China, Southeast Asia, South America, and Mexico found havens of refuge, freedom, and prosperity in their new homelands. Just as chili peppers added flavour to the Old World cuisines, they have likewise added a new energy to the cuisine of their 'new' home far away from its roots. Now, in the 21st century, they are consumed worldwide. In these non-traditional chili pepper countries, chili peppers have become quite common and can be found by the bushel full in every imaginable colour, shape, and level of hotness in many supermarkets as well as in traditional Asian food markets in towns large and small.

Physical Properties of the Chili Pepper and an explanation of their "Hotness"

Mature chili peppers have a rainbow of colours with the most common being green, yellow, orange and fire engine red as well as purple and brown. Likewise they develop into a wide variety of different shapes from long/thin to long/squat rounds, their flavour ranging from mild and sweet to hot and spicy. The hot varieties are the most cultivated. Perhaps this is where their reputation as aphrodisiacs originates, as the colour red is often associated with heat, anger, passion and sexual energy. These fruits not only added spice to food but also to one's sex life so they were considered to be aphrodisiacs for both men and women.

The intensity of red stimulates the body's appetite including the sexual appetite - just think of the infamous red light district in Amsterdam! The shapes too can be considered as aphrodisiacs; the long and narrow shape being phallic in nature while the rounder shapes resemble a woman's curvy hips. But then, many foods have physical shapes, which could be aphrodisiac in nature such as the infamous banana, oysters, bosc pears, *etc.* The next time you go to a restaurant or are invited over for dinner, note the colour of the dining room. One mature chili pepper can have as much vitamin C as 2-6 oranges, which substantially increase the absorption of iron from beans and grains. Carotenoids are mainly responsible for the red colour of some chili peppers. The peppers mature colour (red) indicates that they have high amounts of carotene, both a vitamin A precursor as well as an antioxidant. The 'hotness' of all hot chili peppers including Jalapeño, Habañero, Tabasco pepper, Scotch bonnet, South American Rocoto and Aji as well as the Bhut Jolokia comes from the capsaicinoids, a group of six structurally related compounds belonging to a much larger family called vanilloids. The pungency of a chili pepper is dependent upon the concentration of the capsaicinoids. Capsaicinoids are formed from fatty acids and vanillylamine condensation. These capsaicinoids are naturally colourless, odourless, and also flavourless as all substances do not have any inherent colour, shape, odour, taste, or texture until they come into contact with the sensory nervous system. As much as they are 'afraid' of water they just 'love' oils and fats all the more, hence their addition to the oil early in the meal preparation process. Being able to withstand cooking temperatures they are stable to both hot and cold temperatures as well as time. The two major capsaicinoids, capsaicin and dihyrocapsaicin, account for 80-90% of the total capsaicinoid content and, just like all the capsaicinoids, they are produced by special glands at the juncture of the wall and the white placental tissue, and are spread unevenly throughout the interior of the pod. The white placental tissue including the interior veins or ribs have the most capsaicin with the seeds themselves having no inherent heat although some can be found on the seeds themselves, just like the morphine from the opium pod contaminating the exterior of the poppy seeds.

Seed Dispersion & Germination

These capsaicinoids help the chili pepper plants to spread their seeds abroad as they have developed a unique relationship with indigenous birds such as laenias and thrashers who are attracted to the intense fruit colours. In order to spread their seeds, the seeds either have to stay in the gut longer or have a thicker outer coat. The avian population is the most common seed dispenser. Capsaicin increases the amount of time that the seeds stay in the birds' digestive tract although the time is different for different birds, *i.e.* it decreases intestinal motility. Interestingly, capsaicinoids do not affect birds whatsoever as their tissues do not have any receptors (*i.e.* sensors) chemically sensitive to them but they are both external and internal irritants to mammals. At least in *C. annuum*, a chili pepper family that includes a lot of hot chilies and the common sweet bell pepper, the fruit chemistry is well matched with the seed coat morphology and also with the birds' physiology. Capsaicin extends gut retention time for most seeds but is not always coupled with higher viability (ability to germinate) or longer germination retention rates (number of days the seeds remain viable after being deposited by the birds). Peppers which do not have capasaicin have developed other mechanisms to extend their stay in the birds' gut by

90

having a thicker seed coat. In some non *C. annuum* pepper species, the viability of the seeds is more dependent on the thickness and composition of the seed coat and bird physiology than on capsaicin content. Mammals are not good seed dispersers, at least where the chili peppers are concerned, as they have a much smaller geographical range and the seeds experience physical forces such as chewing and chemical forces such as exposure to digestive enzymes and gut fermentation that renders the seeds non-viable. The capsaicinoids protect the seeds in the fruit from attack by the fungus *Fusarium*, and may also act as allelochemicals to plants in the grass family as they inhibit their growth. It is not known, however, if this also applies to the seeds dropped by the birds as it is unclear if the capsaicinoids remain on the seeds during their brief passage. It is believed that the seeds that have gone through a bird's digestive system actually speed up germination. The bird guano is a source of nutrients for the young germinating plant as well as acting as a deterrent to animals.

Pungency & Factors that Influence Heat

Having the remarkable ability to induce a sharp burst of heat, chili peppers are often referred to as being piquant, or as having a quality of pungency (from the Latin word, 'pungere', to sting or to prick (Dictionary, 2011). The pungency of a chili pepper is dependent upon the concentration of the capsaicinoids. In many eastern countries, pungency is considered to be one of the five tastes along with sour, bitter, sweet, and salty. According to these countries, while flavour is an important characteristic for classifying foods, a food's affect on the body should also be taken into consideration. Western countries, on the other hand, believe that pungency should not be characterized as a fifth taste. It is their belief that because humans do not contain receptors or nerves that react to pungency like they do for the other tastes, it cannot be similarly characterized. Pungency is "tasted" due to their extreme reactions to the mouth and skin. Therefore, while pungency may evoke strong adverse reactions similar to foods that are sour or sweet, because of this technical difference, Westerners separate pungency from the rest of the four tastes. Pungency is measured by using Scoville Units (SHU), which measures the amount of capsaicin (the source of the pepper's heat) in each pepper. While the seeds contain only a low concentration of capsaicin, the level of heat in a pepper is influenced by both the growing conditions and age of the fruit itself. For example, the amount of capsaicin will increase under dry, stressful conditions and, eleven days after the fruit sets, the capsaicin level will begin to decrease. Sun-drying generally reduces the capsaicin content but when the fruits are air dried with minimum exposure to sunlight, the concentration levels are at their peak. Pure capsaicin has the highest rating with 16,000,000 SHU, a pretty hot deal! Nevertheless, the good news is that it is all downhill from there. Most "chili heads" would probably prefer the Hall of Fame member called the Trinidad Scorpion Butch T Pepper, the hottest rated chili pepper in the world with an incredible 1,463,700 SHU. The Habañero (Latin and North America) and Scot Bonnet (Caribbean Islands) have a relatively more manageable 100,000-350,000 SHU. Still more manageable, especially to chili pepper newbies, would be the Tabasco (Mexico), Aji (Peru) or Cayenne (USA) peppers with 30,000-50,000 SHU or even the milder Jalapeño (Mexico) with 2,500 –8,000 SHU. The mildest member of the Capsicum family is the bell pepper. The bell pepper, as a result of a recessive gene that eliminates the production of capsaicin, has a rating of 0. If you desire a little 'heat', however, try the Italian Pepperoncini ,or the Hungarian or Spanish Paprikas which have a 100-500 SHU rating. In terms of pepper sprays, the Bhut Jolokia is a prime candidate and is being used as the deterrent of choice in the United States. Western police in general report to be using a grade of pepper spray that has a Scoville rating of 2,000,000 while the commercial grade is 2,000,000 - 5,300, 000. Regardless, it is clear that there is a wide array

of types and uses for chili peppers. Pungency is dependent on the perception of irritation.

Capsaicin irritates the trigeminal nerves which causes the mouth to burn and the neck, face and

chest to perspire. The amount of pepper needed to cause the burning sensation varies among

people and has no specific dosage that can be quantified. This is partly because our bodies are

able to adapt very quickly to changes in the environment. When the same stimulus is presented

for a significant amount of time, the receptors undergo a process called adaptation. This

essentially means that the receptors accept the signal as routine and the messages in the brain

begin to weaken its intensity. While chili peppers, however, are known to have health benefits

(such as aiding in digestion and circulation), researchers in Mexico and the United States found

that the highest risk for gastric cancer occurred in patients who consumed the most capsaicin.

How Our Body Detects "Heat"

When it comes to food, many people prefer the hottest. The intense burning sensation is

found quite appealing, a culinary thrill. In some sense, one can say that it is mind over matter as

the capsaicinoids 'fool' the body's defense mechanisms. So, how does the body actually 'detect'

the 'hotness' of chili peppers? The capsaicinoids bind with nociceptors located in the lips,

mouth and the back of the throat, which are capable of detecting the temperature in foods, an

important protective mechanism. But upon meeting the capsaicinoids, these nociceptive neurons

send a signal to the brain's fire alarms; "Fire, fire, the body is in physical danger (from burning)

send help immediately!"

The brain responds to this 'false alarm' by sending out the fire brigade, the greater the

alarm the more intense the efforts of the brigade! And in some cases it must be a five alarmer, especially with that hottie Bhut Jolokia from India! The brigade consists of inflammatory mediators released by the body designed to remove the stimulus creating the injury, and aid the healing procedure to the affected tissue. It does this by increasing the rate of blood circulation (the blood removes heat from the tissues and transports white blood cells), opening pores in the skin (releases heat from the blood) and starts the body's own air conditioner, flushing, producing those pearly beads of water on your forehead and under your armpits, a runny nose, and watery eyes. All systems designed to release water as it is a good way to dissipate heat! These effects are especially useful in tropical and sub-tropical climates as they cool the body quite effectively.

Have you ever wondered why you feel hotter on a hot humid day? On a humid day the body is unable to release the heat generated from normal metabolism from the skin into the environment. Hence the moisture stays on your skin, and you feel warmer than normal as thermoreceptors also are at work here. A 2008 study demonstrated that when capsaicin is present, it alters the shape of a protein molecule so that it can no longer do its job by moving excess chemicals called calcium ions out from the cell... no work, no energy use. The interior of the cells eventually builds up a lot of excess energy that, in an effort to maintain peaceful harmony within the cell, releases the energy as physical heat.

Membrane Receptors and the Effect they have on the Temperature of the Cell

The cells and the different organelles within the cell are surrounded by a membrane in which there are pores or channels of various sizes, which let substances in or out of the cell. The opening and closing of these channels are regulated by sensors affected (stimulated or inhibited) by either the bonding of chemicals and/or by electrical signals originating from either inside or outside of the cell. In the capsaicin case, they bind to certain members of a large family of sensors called TRPV receptors (Transient Receptor Potential Vanilloids), a strange but most accurate descriptive code used by scientists to differentiate between and also identify all the various sensors. Scientists have determined that humans have six different TRPV receptors, each numbered from 1-6 that are involved in a variety of physiological functions. Located in the brain, bladder, kidney, bowel and skin, the TRPV1 receptor is activated by a large variety of both physical and chemical stimuli, noxious stimuli which can potentially cause physical harm to the body, the best examples being capsaicin, temperatures greater than 43°C, and substances with low pH. These TRPV receptors are found in many different tissues and organs and are involved in the sensing of a variety of physical temperatures that aid the body in regulating internal temperature. This is important as temperature extremes are capable of causing damage to tissues by affecting the fluidity of cell membranes, hence their functionality. Cell membranes are composed of two layers of lipids and fats that organize themselves in a specific pattern based on their dislike for water, their 'fear' ranging from small to great. The more fearful they are of water the more likely they will put these parts as far away from water as possible. The colder temperatures cause the lipids and fats to become more solid with the membranes becoming more rigid while warmer temperatures cause the same lipids and fats to become too fluid with the membranes potentially losing their physical integrity. Just try putting a cup of fat in the refrigerator and see what happens. Then take the same cup out and gently warm it... what happens to the fat? Capsaicin binds to the TRPV1 receptor located on nociceptive neurons causing an influx of calcium ions, leading to an excitation of these neurons. The activation of these neurons is what causes you to feel that burning sensation without actually "burning" your tongue. The cell sets off the brain's alarm bells and calls out the fire brigade which 'races out the door' to the put out the fire which, ironically, does not even exist! But the cell is not charged nor fined for the false alarm.

Release of Endorphins & Their Effects

The steady 'burn' induced by the capsaicinoids also cause the release of a large amount of endorphins, the body's natural painkillers. When a chili pepper is ingested, the chemical compound capsaicin binds to receptor S on the taste buds found within the papillae of the tongue called 'transient receptor vanilloid-1'. When this binding occurs, a section of the receptor called 'PIP2' breaks off, and allows calcium to enter the cell. Once calcium enters the cells, a chemical known as 'substance P' (a neurotransmitter) is activated, and sends a signal of pain to the brain. The brain responds to this signal by releasing a chemical known as 'β-endorphins' that are able to bind to μ-opioid receptors located on the spinal cord. These are the same receptors in which chemicals derived from opium, such as morphine, are able to bind.

As β-endorphins are bound to the μ-opioid receptors, a neurotransmitter called 'GABA' is no longer produced while another neurotransmitter known as 'dopamine' is produced in excess amounts. Excessive release of the chemical dopamine is shown to provide a feeling of euphoria that lasts for several hours, proving it to be an effective painkiller which unfortunately may have addictive effects (as seen with individuals addicted to opium derived chemicals). It is this very 'pain for pleasure' experience that causes so many individuals to incorporate chili peppers into their diet on a regular basis. But as with other psychoactive 'drugs' one can build up a chili pepper tolerance.

Chili Pepper Tolerance

You may know someone who eats spicy food all the time but does not seem to be as affected by the heat in comparison to other people. This difference in perception is caused by two things; tolerance, and taster category. Tolerance to chili heat can be built up after repeated exposure to capsaicinoids, because the level of 'Substance P' declines. Substance P is a neurotransmitter, so it is responsible for transmitting the signal from a cell in your body that has had TRPV 1 activated by capsaicin to your brain, where it is then perceived as pain and heat. So when the levels of Substance P subside, these signals have a tough time getting through and a person becomes less affected by a certain amount of chili pepper. The second difference between people that seem to have superhuman tolerance to chilies is whether a person is a supertaster, taster or non-taster. Basically the category a person belongs to is determined by the number of taste buds on the fungi form papillae (the little bumps) on their tongue. Tasters have about 5000 taste buds on each papilla, with supertasters having more and non-tasters less. The more taste buds present, the more sensitive a person is to flavours in general, including chili heat. The combination of tolerance and number of taste buds account for the variety of reactions observed when different people eat the same amount of spice. There is no predetermined amount of pepper that can produce the same psychoactive effect in humans.

Medical Applications

As previously mentioned, chili peppers are capable of releasing endorphins which give it a "pain-killing" quality as well as creating a long lasting desensitization to pain and discomfort. The chili pepper is effective in treating Postherpetic Neuralgia (PHN), a condition that causes pain because of severe nerve damage caused by shingles. The peppers are incorporated into an ointment, that when absorbed, reduces pain signals sent to the brain. Furthermore, this same effect can relieve those with Diabetic Neuropathy, sufferers of arthritis, backaches, sprains, strains and itching and inflammation for patients with psoriasis. Therefore, although when ingested chili peppers can create a "burning" sensation, when used in the form of an ointment it is an effective pain killer that reduces the amount of "Substance P", which transmits pain throughout the body.

Preventing Depression & Applications for Weight Loss

Feeling blue? You might want to include chili peppers in your next meal. A study from the National University Hospital in Copenhagen found that capsaicin releases betaendorphins - natural stimulants that produce a feeling of euphoria (as mentioned earlier). Other research on the role capsaicin can play in the treatment of serious depression focuses on TRVP1 receptors. Pharmacologists from Brown University discovered that blocking the TRVP1 receptor in the brain had a positive impact on reducing long-term depression. They believe that manipulating the TRPV1 receptors may have an extended effect on physiological behaviour, potentially providing sustained relief to those suffering from depression. If you're dieting, capsaicin may be the extra help you're looking for to enhance weight loss. Studies have shown that capsaicin decreases appetite. This might make it easier to resist nibbling between meals and may decrease overall caloric intake. Researchers also believe that capsaicin decreases the amount of ghrelin produced; a hormone that promotes hunger. And that's not all - capsaicin has also been found to both break down and inhibit the production of body fat. In one clinical study, rats on a high-fat diet that were also given capsaicin ended up being 8% leaner than the rats on high-fat alone. In addition, several studies have shown that capsaicin helps us burn calories by increasing thermogenesis. By inhibiting hunger, preventing fat cell formation, and increasing metabolism, chili peppers may be the perfect diet aid. Plus, capsaicin can add flavour and spark to traditional diet food, making it more satisfying. Furthermore, capsaicin's euphoric effect may make you feel so good that you are able to resist eating out of boredom, or sadness *etc.* So by now your brain has probably experienced somewhat of a chili pepper information overload but hopefully you have found a new respect for these hot guys. Being knowledgeable of the effects of the temperature sensitive TRVP1 receptor, you can explain to your friends, over some hot and spicy pork ribs the fascinating world of how the consumption of certain foods may promote cooling or heating sensations. The cooling effect of peppermint or the spiciness of black pepper, ginger, garlic, onion, horseradish, wasabi, mustard, radish, can be explained by their respective bioactive compounds affecting different types of receptors on cells. "The force is with you" as your chili pepper knowledge has perked up and given you just the thing you need to 'spice-up' your next backyard barbeque! And remember to regularly indulge in chili peppers as they are just about the kindest and nicest thing you can do for yourself. So, go ahead, indulge intelligently, live high by spicing your life and your food with chili peppers ... buon appetito!

Glossary

Action potential: the change in electrical potential that occurs between the inside and outside of a nerve or muscle fibre when it is stimulated, serving to transmit nerve signals.

Analgesic: a substance that relieves pain.

Arthritis: painful inflammation and stiffness of the joints.

Capsaicin: a colorless, pungent, crystalline compound that is derived from the capsicum pepper and is a strong irritant to skin and mucous membranes.

Carotenoids: any of a class of mainly yellow, orange, or red fat-soluble pigments, including carotene, which give color to plant parts such as ripe tomatoes and autumn leaves.

Diabetes: A disorder of the metabolism causing excessive thirst and the production of large amounts of urine.

Dopamine: A compound present in the body as a neurotransmitter and a precursor of other substances including epinephrine.

Endorphin: Any of a group of hormones secreted within the brain and nervous system and having a number of physiological functions.

Euphoric: Something that brings about a feeling of happiness, confidence, or well-being.

Fatty acid: A carboxylic acid consisting of a hydrocarbon chain and a terminal carboxyl group.

Germinate: To begin to grow from a seed, and put out shoots after a period of dormancy.

Guano: The excrement of seabird.

Inflammation: A localized physical condition in which part of the body becomes reddened, swollen, hot, and often painful, esp. as a reaction to injury or infection.

Neuron: A specialized cell that conducts nerve impulses.

Neuropeptide: Any of the various peptides found in neural tissue, such as endorphins and enkephalins.

Neurotransmitter: A chemical substance that is released at the end of a nerve fiber by the arrival of a nerve impulse and, by diffusing across the synapse or junction, causes the transfer of the impulse to another nerve fiber, a muscle fiber, or some other structure,

Nociceptor: A sensory receptor that responds to potentially damaging stimuli by sending nerve signals to the spinal cord and brain, which usually causes the perception of pain.

Noxious: harmful, poisonous, or very unpleasant.

Organelles: A specialized structure in a cell, such as a mitochondrion.

Papillae: A small rounded protrusion on a part or organ of the body.

PIP2: Also known as phosphatidylinositol 4,5-bisphosphate, it is a minor phospholipid component of cell membranes.

Psoriasis: A chronic skin disease characterized by circumscribed red patches covered with white scales.

Psychoactive: Affecting the mind.

Receptor: A region of tissue, or a molecule in a cell membrane, that responds specifically to a particular neurotransmitter, hormone, antigen, or other substance.

Thermogenesis: The production of heat.

Thermoreceptors: A nerve ending sensitive to stimulation by heat.

Transient Receptor Potential Vanilloids receptors (TRPVR): A descriptive code used by scientists to differentiate and identify various sensors.

References

Abraham-Juarez, M. R.; Rocha-Granados, M. C.; Lopez, M. G.; Rivera- Bustamante, R. F.; Ochoa-Alejo, N. 2008. Virus- induced silencing of Comt, pAmt and Kas genes results in a reduction of capsaicinoid accumulation in chili pepper fruits. *Planta*, 227, 681-695.

Appendino, G.; Minassi, A.; Pagani, A.; and Ech-Chabad, A. 2008. The Role of Natural products in the Ligan Deorphanization of TRP Channels. *Current Pharmaceutical Design*, 14, 2-17.

Bach, F. W. 2008. ß-endorphin in the brain. A role in nociception. *Acta Anaesthesiologica Scandinavica*. 41(1), 133-140.

Balch, P. 2003. *Prescription for dietary wellness*. New York: Penguin Group (USA) Inc. Barry G. Green. 2005. Lingual Heat and Cold Sensitivity Following Exposure to Capsaicin or Menthol. *Chemical Senses*, 30 (Supplement 1), 201-202.

Bandell, M.; Macpherson, L. J.; and Patappoutan, A. 2007. From chills to chilis: mechanisms for thermosensation and chemesthesis via thermo TRPs. *Current Opinion in Neurobiology*, 17, 490-497.

Bartoshuk, L. (n.d.). A Taste Illusion: Taste Sensation Localized by Touch. Retrieved from http://www.bijouterieleroy.com/riedel3.htm

Bosland, P. W.; and Baral, J. B. 2007. 'Bhut Jolokia'-The World's Hottest Known Chile Pepper is a Putative Naturally Occurring Interspecific Hybrid. *Horticultural Science*, 42, 222-224.

Schulze, Birgit and Dieter Spiteller. 2009. Capsaicin: Tailored Chemical Defence Against Unwanted "Frugivores". *Chemicaly Biochemistry*, 10(3), 428-429.

Brett, A. Cromer and Peter McIntyre. 2008. Mini-review: Painful toxins acting at TRPV1. *Toxicon*, 51, 163-173.

Chemical and Engineering News. 2003. Red Hot Chili Peppers. Accessed on May 19th 2010 from http://pubs.acs.org/cen/whatstuff/stuff/8144peppers.html

Chemical and Engineering News, November 3rd, 2003. Red Hot Chili Peppers. Accessed on May 19th 2010 from http://pubs.acs.org/cen/whatstuff/stuff/8144peppers.html

Costa, R. M.; Liu, L.; Nicolelis, M. A. L.; and Simon. S. A. 2005. Gustatory Effects of Capsaicin that are Independent of TRPV1 Receptors. *Chemical Senses*, 30 (Supplement 1), 198-200.
Cromer, B. A.; and McIntyre, P. 2008. Mini-review: Painful toxins acting at TRPV1. *Toxicon,* 51, 163-173.

Cronin, R. 2004. The Chili Pepper's Pungent Principle. *Alternative and Complimentary Therapies*, 8(2), 110-113.

De Felipe, C. *et. al*. 1998. Altered nociception, analgesia and aggression in mice lacking the receptor for substance P. *Nature,* 392, 394-397.

Dictionary.Com. 2011. Pungency. Retrieved July 19, 2011, from, http://dictionary.reference.com/browse/pungency

Duman, A. D. 2010. Storage of red chili pepper under hermetically sealed or vacuum conditions for preservation of its quality and prevention of mycotoxin occurrence. *Journal of Stoned Products Research*. 46, 155-160.

Galgani, J. E.; and Ravussin, E. 2010. Effect of dihydrocapsiate on resting metabolic rate in humans. *American Journal of Clinical Nutrition*. 92(5), 1089-1093.

Gibson, H .E.; Edwards, J .G.; Page, R .S.; Van Hook, M .J.; and Kauer, J. A. 2008. TRPV1 channels mediate long-term depression at synapses on hippocampal interneurons. *Neuron*, 57(5): 746-759.

Green, B. G. 2005. Lingual Heat and Cold Sensitivity Following Exposure to Capsaicin or Menthol. *Chemical Senses*, 30 (Supplement 1), 201-202.

Hayman, M.; and Kam, P. C. A. 2008. Capsaicin: A review of its pharmacology and clinical applications. *Current Anaesthesia and Clinical Care*, 19, 338-343.

Jordt, S. E.; Ehrlich, B .E. 2007. TRP Channels in Disease. In Calcium Signalling in Disease, Molecular Pathology of Calcium, Ernesto Carafoli and Marisa Brini (eds.), Springer, Netherlands.

Julius, D. *et al.* 1997. The capsaicin receptor: A heat-activated ion channel in the pain pathway. *Nature*. 389, 816-824.

Kato-Noguchi, N.; and Tan*aka*, Y. 2003. Effects of capsaicin on plant growth. *Biologia Plantarum*, 47(1), 157-159.

Lejeune, Manuela, P. G. M..; Kovacs, E.M.R.; and Westerterp-Plantenga, M. S. 2003. Effect of capsaicin on substrate oxidation and weight maintenance after modest body-weight loss in human subjects. *British Journal of Nutrition*, 90, 651-659.

Luo, X. J., Peng, J., Li Y .J. 2011. Recent advances in the study on capsaicinoids and capsinoids. *European Journal of Pharmacology*. 650, 1-7.

Mathur, R.; Dangi, R .S.; Dass, S. C.; and Malhotra, R .C. 2000. The hottest chili variety in India. *Current Science*, 79(3), 287-288. Scientific correspondence.

Mortensen, M. J.; Mortensen, E. J. 2009. The Power of Capsaicin. Continuing *Education Topics & Issues*, 11, 1, 8-12.

Mueller- Seitz, E.; Hiepler, C.; Petz, M. 2008. Chili Pepper Fruits: Content and Pattern of Capsaicinoids in Single Fruits of Different Ages. *Journal of Agricultural Food Chemistry*, 56, 12114-12121.

Nagy, I.; Sántha, P.; Jancsó, G; and Urbán, L. 2004. The role of the vanilloid (capsaicin) receptor (TRPV1) in physiology and pathology. *European Journal of Pharmacology*, 500, 351-369.

Oral Allergy Syndrome Treatment Detailed Information. (n.d.) *Fungiform Papillae Information*. Retrieved from: http://oralallergy.net/fungiform-papillae.html

Prout, L. 2000. *Live in the balance: The ground-breaking east-west nutrition program.* New York: Marlowe & Company.

Ratey, J. 2000. *A user's guide to the brain: perception, attention, and the four theatre of the brain.* New York: Random House.

Schulze, B.; and Spiteller, D. 2009. Capsaicin: Tailored Chemical Defense against Unwanted "Frugivores". *Chem Biochem*, 10(3), 428-429.

Siemens, J.; Zhou, S.; Piskorowski, R.; Nikai, T.; Lumpkin, E.A.; Basbaum, A. I.; King, D.; and Julius, D. 2006. Spider toxins activate the capsaicin receptor to produce inflammatory pain. *Nature*, 444, 208-212.

Smeets, A. J.; Westerterp-Plantenga, M. S. 2009. The acute effects of a lunch containing capsaicin on energy and substrate utilization, hormones, and satiety. *European Journal of Nutrition*. 48(4), 229-234.

Starowicz, K.; Cristino, L.; and Di Marzo, V. 2008. TRPV1 Receptors in the Central Nervous System: Potential for Previously Unforeseen Therapeutic Applications. *Current Pharmaceutical Design*, 14, 42-54.

Stewart, C. J.; Mazourek, M.; Stellari, G. M.; O'Connell, M.; Jahn, M. 2007. Genetic control of pungency in C. chinense via the Pun1 locus. *Journal of Experimental Botany*, 38, 979 -991.

Story, G. M.; and Cruz-Orengo, L. 2007. Feel the Heat. *American Scientist*, 95, 326-333.

Tanaka, Y.; Hosokawa, M.; Otsu, K.; Watanabe, T.; Yazawa, S. 2009. Assessment of Capsiconinoid Composition, Nonpungent Capsaicinoid Analogues, in Capsicum Cultivars. *Journal of Agricultural Food Chenmistry*. 57, 5407- 5412

Thyme, J. 2009. *HOT! Make your own sauce*. United States: Chet Beates. Tremblay, A. *et al.* (2006). Metabolic effects of spices, teas, and caffeine. *Physioy of .Behavior,* 89(1), 85-91.

Tweksbury, J.J.; Levey, D.J.; Huizinga, M.; Haak, D. C. and Treveset, A. 2008. Costs and benefits of capsaicin mediated control of gut retention in dispersers of wild chilies. *Ecology*, 89(1), 107-117.

Urbán, L. 2004. The role of the vanilloid (capsaicin) receptor (TRPV1) in physiology and pathology. *European Journal of Pharmacology*, 500, 351-369.

Venkatachalam, K.; and Montell, C. 2007. TRP Channels. *Annual Reviews in Biochemistry*, 76, 387-417.

Vriens, J.; Nilius, B.; and Vennekens. R. 2008. Herbal Compounds and Toxins Modulating TRP Channels. *Current Neuropharmacology*, 6, 79-96.

Westerterp-Plantenga, M. S.; Smeets, A.; and Lejeune, M. P.G. 2005. Sensory and gastrointestinal satiety effects of capsaicin on food intake. *International Journal of Obesity*, 29, 682-688.

Wolf, J.E. *et al.* 1993. A double-blind evaluation of topical capsaicin in pruritic psoriasis. *Journal of the American Academy of Dermatology*. 29(3), 438-442.

Wright, C.A. 2007. The Medieval Spice Trade and the Diffusion of the Chile. *Gastronomica, the Journal of Food and Culture*, 7(2), 35-43.

Yun, J.W. *et al.* 2010. Proteomic analysis for antiobesity potential of capsaicin on white adipose tissue in rats fed with a high fat diet. *Journal of Proteome Research.* 9(6), 2977-87.

Zhang, W.Y. & Li Wan Po, A. 1994. The effectiveness of topically applied capsaicin. A meta-analysis. *European Journal of Clinical Pharmacology*. 46, 517-22.

§ 4:

Getting your high from ginseng!

All over the country there are students drinking coffee, Red Bulls and other forms of 'energy' drinks to try and stay up those extra couple of hours in hopes of gaining a few more pages of information for exams and assignments. Even though coffee works to keep you up for those few extra hours, there are a few unwanted side effects including lack of concentration, retaining the information you are reading, nervousness and irritability. As these students start realizing that their coffee diet isn't the greatest, they start looking for other forms of stimulation. As they do a little bit of research they come across the ancient Oriental herb from the genus *Panax* called ginseng. Now being prepared for your study groups and all night study marathons, you start to wonder what else ginseng can do for you. There are many different strains of ginseng that are available and all are believed to be beneficial. There has not been a lot of valid research on this legendary herb so there is no evidence that it actually works. The Oriental culture, however, has been using it for centuries, so it must be doing something. Ginseng has been known to help boost energy and is one of the reasons it is added to energy drinks. It has also been known to relieve stress, which can help students during exam season. There are a few forms of ginseng that are different but do have the same characteristics. One example of this would be Siberian ginseng which has had some Russian studies prove that it has the same effects as the *Panax* strain. Ginseng is a safe and easy way to boost energy as well as overall health.

Ginseng has been the focus of many legends, superstitions, and much misunderstanding. It is a plant that was discovered and used as a food source 5000 years ago in Manchuria (northeast China). Consuming the ginseng roots gave beneficial effects and has been used as a medicine for the last 2000 years. The old Chinese Cannon of Medicine states that ginseng "…strengthens the soul, brightens the eyes, opens the heart, expels evil, benefits understanding, and if taken for prolonged periods of time will invigorate the body and prolong life." As an ordinarily slow and low growing perennial forest plant, it has intrigued many people due to its various magical curative properties. *Panax ginseng* is the best known and most used of all Oriental herbs, often referred to as the 'The King of Herbs' in Asia for its ability to boost energy and vitality while improving health and performance. The word *Panax* refers to "all healing", which is believed to have the properties of healing any part of the body. Some of the known medical effects of ginseng are: as an adaptogen, anti-inflammatory, antioxidant, aphrodisiac, and the ability to reduce the risk of cancer (anticancer effects). Ginseng products, or tonics, are also known to give invigorating and strengthening qualities. It was thought to fix the imbalances in the Yin-Yang life force, and restore "Qi", a Chinese word referring to energy flow.

There are eleven different types of ginseng and they grow very slowly in shaded regions, requiring the same climate and weather in the northern hemisphere as wheat and corn. *Panax ginseng* is the four-seasonal plant group whose name came from the Greek goddess of healing as it is related to cures. *Panax ginseng* is commonly known as Chinese Ginseng. The word 'renshen' is a Chinese word meaning 'man root' because when ginseng is 5 to 6 years old its physical appearance resembles the human body. In Asia, genuine ginseng is known to be Chinese and Red Korean ginseng but this group includes Japanese and Vietnamese ginseng. There is one ginseng in North America included in the '*Panax*' group that is used by its indigenous people. There are also certain plants that go by the name of 'ginseng' but do not belong to the *Panax* group, even though they have the word 'ginseng' as part of their name. While most "herbs are thought to strengthen your resistance to all kinds of stress while enhancing your energy", they do not contain the same "beneficial effects on living matter" as the Panax group. The most famous non-ginseng, the Siberian ginseng, is a small woody shrub that was sold in North America as a ginseng.

Ever since its initial usage, the demand for ginseng in China has always been high. By the early 1900s, both Korea and the United States started the first commercial cultivation as the demand for wild ginseng caused sharp declines in the wild stocks. Now an astonishing 95% of ginseng grown in the United States and Canada is exported to China. In 1975, both wild Asian and American ginseng were placed on Schedule II of the Convention on International Trade in Endangered Species (CITES), an international agreement among nations aimed to protect the native wild animals and plants from extinction due to over-harvesting, slow root re-growth, and habitat loss. Both wild Asian and American ginseng are considered to be threatened species meaning that the CITES listing prohibits any and all illegal export of these two wild native ginsengs from their native countries, but export of cultivated ginseng must be accompanied by permits. According to Environment Canada, however, this only applies to the whole ginseng plant; therefore this does not prohibit the export of ginseng seeds or other derivatives. Ginseng harvested from completely wild sources is the rarest and the most coveted, despite the fact that is it illegal. With an underground price starting at US $600 per pound (this increases substantially with age and appearance), it is a very secretive and money-making trade. All Asian and North American ginseng in the commercial market is now farmed under 'artificial' shade causing a need for approximately $50 per pound, but the roots do not have the desired appearance. More importantly, however, these roots contain different numbers, types, and concentration of the ginsenosides regardless whether the root is Asian or North American. Ginseng roots grown in wild shaded forests yield a product similar to the wild ginseng in physical appearance and chemical composition. While these roots are still considered 'simulated' or even 'artificial' in some countries, these wood-cultivated ginseng plants may just be the next best thing to grow among forest trees influencing their desirable characteristics.

American and Asian ginseng roots contain genocides; naturally occurring chemical compounds believed to contribute towards better health. The group Supportive Care in Cancer conducted a 2010 study, in which participants that took American Ginseng over a period of eight weeks showed a greater vitality improvement when compared to those on a placebo. Similarly, Asian ginseng is used to support the health of people recovering from illness. Despite the above study, NCCAM states: "Although Asian ginseng has been widely studied for a variety of uses, research results to date do not conclusively support health claims associated with the herb." This means research has not been conducted thoroughly enough to eliminate bias and reach a decisive conclusion on ginseng's properties. By extension, this would also make it difficult to determine other factors that may influence ginseng's properties.

The root is the main part of the ginseng plant, which has been used by Native North Americans as traditional medicines. Other parts of the plant that can be used are the rootlets, leaves, and berries. These parts may have beneficial properties in reducing the risk of obesity and diabetes. The root of the plant can be used in either fresh or dried forms, however the processing method in which the ginseng is dried under the sun influences the presence, activity, and bioavailability of its active compounds. The process of sun drying involves the ginseng being placed in bamboo or wooden shelves that are placed under the sun. When they are dried to a certain level they are baked under a low temperature and moved outdoor once more to be dried under the sun again. The dried ginseng here is referred to as White Ginseng as per Exploration of Ginseng Plantation and Processing. This method is suitable for the general body type because it is mild and naturally dried. White Ginseng can be placed in a closed steam chamber where steam slowly changes the White Ginseng into a Red Ginseng. Once steamed, they are transferred outdoors and cooled to remove any moisture. Red Ginseng is very warm in nature and it can inhibit the breakdown of active ingredients, but an over dosage can lead to headaches, insomnia, palpitations, and a rise in blood pressure. There are three types of fresh White Ginseng categorized into type A, B and C ginsenosides. Type A is known to suppress hemolysis and inhibit the central nervous system and Types B and C show hemolytic activity and activate the central nervous system. They all have dual regulatory functions. Certain ginsenosides (along with M1) that are water soluble get metabolized by intestinal bacteria in the gastrointestinal tract (or the GI tract) and the products are then absorbed into the mucosa and transported into the bloodstream. Other ginsenosides that are composed of fat, however, are metabolized comparatively slower and are insoluble.

Recently, optimal brain functioning and brain health have received greater focus not only from aging baby boomers but from the younger generations as well. It has become common knowledge that factors such as physical and chemical brain damage as well as emotional stress can impair the functioning of the brain as well as the production and transmission of chemicals in the brain. These chemicals, called neurotransmitters, are responsible for a variety of functions from mood, to memory, and movement. Damage to the brain can also directly affect the functioning to the central nervous system (CNS) which receives its direction from the brain. People are now turning to non-prescription drugs as an effort to increase both general health and brain health. Ginseng and ginko biloba are two examples of natural remedies that are taken for brain health, increased brain function, and to minimize effects of any previous damage to the brain.

Quantity is not always better than quality! Ginsenosides are slowly absorbed in small concentrations across the blood-brain barrier. Ginseng dosage is extremely important and it is recommended to continually lower the long-term dosage, as it may have a negative hormone-like effect with prolonged usage. When used in the right dosage ginsenosides are extremely effective in the body, specifically in the protection of cells. Benefits of using ginseng include the protection of brain tissues from free radicals as a result of trauma or poor diet, increasing blood flow to the brain, protecting the cell from nerve damage and enhancing the growth of nerve development. Ginsenosides also have an effect on the immune system and have been successful in preventing the death of non-diseased cells as well as enhancing the death of diseased cells. Various ginseng extracts, which include Rg1 and Rb1, have been shown to improve spinal cord injuries as well as ischemic brain damage when used with IV therapy. Experimental research suggests a positive relationship between ginseng and neurodegenerative diseases, aging and some CNS disorders. Current research has shown that ginseng improved the cognitive performance in Alzheimer's Disease patients with continued use when compared with those who did not consume the ginseng extract. Ginseng is thought to have a positive effect on neurodegenerative diseases while minimizing the degeneration and death of nerve cells. Research is being done to observe the effect on other neurodegenerative diseases such as Parkinson's, Alzheimer's, Huntington's, Cushing's and Amyotrophic Lateral Sclerosis (ALS).

Ginsenosides help the signals in the brain work faster and better. One area where they are specifically useful is with important chemicals in the brain called "neurotransmitters". The four neurotransmitters that are affected by these active compounds in Ginseng are called serotonin, dopamine, norepinephrine and GABA. These are important chemicals that are responsible for controlling mood, keeping attention, sexual interest, learning, memory, appetite, sleep, and more. Too many or too little of these chemicals can cause problems with brain functions which might lead to mental problems such as anxiety and depression. Two of these compounds found in ginseng are called Rg1 and Rb1. The first one has been known to work more effectively to improve function in the nervous system. The second one, Rb1, helps as well, but to a lesser extent and occasionally will have a negative effect on the nervous system. Different types of ginseng will have different amounts of each of these compounds. For example Asian ginseng has more Rg1, and ginseng from North America has more Rb1. The compound Rb1 is known to elicit a more calm feeling and so the ginseng that comes from North America is known to be more calming.

There are glands in the body that release large amounts of hormones. The three main glands are the hypothalamus, the pituitary gland and the adrenal glands. These hormones are produced to help regulate mood, stress and our body's reaction to it. Some hormones that affect our moods are norepinephrine, dopamine, serotonin and thyroid hormones. Depression can be caused by the imbalances of the above hormones in our brain. The hypothalamus is a small area in the brain that acts as a main security system or a police station. It is constantly on guard to ensure our body is kept safe and well maintained. It does this by "watching" what is happening in the external environment, and in turn causes our bodies to react to it. The hypothalamus will control hormone production by increasing or decreasing concentrations being produced throughout the entire body. The hypothalamus connects our nervous system to the endocrine system (a group of glands, which collect "information" from our body to bring back to the hypothalamus. It can be seen as the police officers, collecting information throughout the body to bring back to the police station) with the use of the pituitary gland which is located below the hypothalamus. The pituitary gland will produce hormones to send a signal to the adrenal glands, which are located on top of each kidney. In turn, the hormones epinephrine, norepinephrine, and cortisol, are produced by the adrenal glands and are then released into the bloodstream.

Serotonin, dopamine, norepinephrine, and GABA are essential to our physical and mental health. There are many things that have an effect on the brain's ability to make and maintain the delicate balance of these essential brain chemicals, including physical or emotional stress, genetics, trauma, lack of sleep, and our modern diet high in both fat and sugars. Shock or trauma (whether it is consciously or subconsciously perceived) as well as stress can cause a response in the hypothalamus. The hypothalamus produces hormones which stimulate the release of other hormones by the pituitary gland, hormones which send signals throughout the body to carry out required functions. When a response is triggered in the hypothalamus, hormones are released to the rest of the body and prepare it for the fight or flight response by increasing blood pressure, pulse rate, respiration, blood sugar levels, body temperature, *etc.* Stress causes further imbalances in the neurotransmitters because there is also increased activity of the enzymes (called monoamine oxidases or MAOs) that break down these neurotransmitters. As GABA is a protein, its concentration is also decreased as protein synthesis is stopped by stress and depression. Due to the very rapid use and replacement of these neurotransmitters, the halted production cannot keep up with increased need. While this is manageable for a short period of time it eventually leads to chronic brain neurotransmitter depletion resulting in the familiar 'burned out' feeling. Constant neurotransmitter depletion can lead to feelings of anxiety, apathy, fear, worthlessness, nervousness, irritability, disordered eating patterns, and unbalanced diets, all symptoms associated with depression.

In the brain, ginsenosides moderate the activity of the MAOs while stimulating protein synthesis, which is essentially the process of building proteins. As proteins are essential nutrients, this process is important because it assists in the creation and maintenance of strong bones and muscles while protecting our bodies from infections and viruses. Furthermore, protein synthesis releases energy and thereby increases metabolic/digestive reactions. Both MAOs and protein synthesis are needed to increase the respective brain neurotransmitter concentration and ratios. A neurotransmitter is a chemical or substance (*e.g.* norepinephrine) by which a nerve cell communicates with another cell, organ, or muscle. There is evidence that people with certain forms of depression, anxiety and Attention Deficit Hyperactivity Disorder do not produce adequate quantities of particular neurotransmitters. Stimulant drugs or herbs, such as ginseng, that are known to increase concentrations of various brain neurotransmitters are typically prescribed. Therefore, with the consistent use of the correct type and dosage of ginseng during some forms of depression or anxiety, one's mood and outlook may become more positive and energizing as the brain neurotransmitters return to their normal levels and relative ratios. Anxiety levels are also decreased by the direct effect of specific ginsenosides on the hippocampus. The hippocampus is a part of the brain that plays a central role in memory encoding and retrieving, learning, spatial orientation, and is a natural mediator of emotion. While the previously discussed fight or flight response is warranted in times of danger, it acts as an impediment when it causes the release of adrenaline from the endocrine gland during times when no danger is present, thereby causing stress and anxiety. The impairment of the hippocampus makes it less likely for an individual to draw upon memory to evaluate the nature of a stressor in ambiguous situations, and makes it easier for other chemicals to affect the release of stressor hormones from the endocrine glands. Therefore, the hippocampus inhibits other messenger chemicals from affecting the endocrine glands. As a result, anxiety levels decrease and the feeling of nervousness and fear are greatly reduced.

As quoted by Wong, "American ginseng may fight mental fatigue during prolonged mental activity." Ginseng will also help you deal with stress by limiting the amount of work the

114

adrenal gland has to do (Simply Ginseng, Adrenal Fatigue Syndrome). When less adrenaline is secreted, the body will not feel as great of a need to initiate a "fight or flight" response. The resulting process generates a calming effect.

Ginsenosides have been proven to have many pharmacological effects, as well as effects in other regions of the brain such as the hippocampus which controls special navigation, long term memory, and complex decisions. Interestingly, the hippocampus is extremely sensitive to increased stress levels for prolonged periods of time. Too much stress leads to a decrease in its physical size and effective functioning. The hippocampus is also the region of the brain which is largely affected by people with Alzheimer's disease and post-traumatic stress disorders. Ginsenosides Rb1 and Rg1 found in red ginseng work by increasing the survival of newly generated nerve cells in the hippocampus and also help to improve memory and learning. These two types of ginsenosides are most commonly found in ginseng root and have been found to adjust and regulate the activity of acetylcholine which is a neurotransmitter in both the brain and the body. In the brain, Rb1 and Rg1 control the release and absorption of acetylcholine as well as the rate it is absorbed into the hippocampus. Additionally, ginsenosides regulate the amount of a certain enzyme that is present which plays a critical role in the production of acetylcholine. The results from lab experiments preformed on rats suggest that these chemicals might help to improve cholinergic functions in humans, meaning that they may be used to treat memory deficits.

Many ginsenosides can be very beneficial in maintaining proper circulation around the body. Certain ginsenosides such as Rg1 can help increase nitric oxide production and vascular tissue development. This reduces high blood pressure and increases blood flow around the body. Therefore essential organs such as the brain and heart get sufficient oxygen and nutrients. This helps maintain cell heath and allows the organs to perform normally. Finally waste removal from the tissues is increased with blood flow, thereby removing substances that can potentially harm the body.

Although the exact mechanism is not clearly understood, improvement in cognitive performance is another CNS benefit of ginseng which affects the hippocampus. This is one of many results from animal studies which cannot be performed on humans due to the moral and ethical implications of such invasive procedures. Some studies have also suggested that ginsenosides also increase dopamine and norepinephrine in the cerebral cortex which is a tissue located in the brain composed of nerve cells. The cerebral cortex has a critical role in memory, attention, perceptual awareness, thought, language, and consciousness. Through the increase in dopamine and norepinephrine levels in the cerebral cortex, ginsenosides are able to favourably affect this tissue by increasing attention, cognitive processing, and integrated sensory-motor function. Essentially, ginsenosides make it easier to focus, acquire and apply information, and quickly react when the senses are stimulated. Additionally, it has been shown that total ginsenoside are able to control and contain the activity in nerve cells stimulated by dopamine, and hence can block behavioural sensitization which is a persistent and enhanced response to a stimulus such as a psychoactive stimulant that leads to long-term sensitivity of the stimulus. Psychoactive stimulants are drugs that have the capacity to become a habit because of their stimulating effect on mood and behaviour. Psychoactive stimulants include morphine, cocaine, methamphetamines and nicotine.

Aside from their antioxidant abilities, ginsenosides also positively affect blood vessels in the body through increased production of nitric oxide (NO). NO is a signalling molecule in the body that encourages the relaxation and dilation of blood vessels. This is how ginsenosides act to improve circulation, brain function and memory. You can see how blood vessel relaxation (which encourages vasodilation) would help in preventing brain damage caused by a blood clot. Taking ginseng would help in the production of NO which in turn would relax the blood vessels allowing blood to pass around the clot and reach the brain, preventing damage to the brain associated with cell death caused by lack of circulation. In addition, the ginsenoside Rg1 has been proven to encourage angiogenesis. Angiogenesis is a physiological process involving the growth of new blood vessels from existing ones. This process does occur naturally in the human body, when healing from a deep cut for example. What is promising about the new blood vessel formation that results from Rg1 is that the new formation occurs in parts of the body that do not experience angiogenesis after adult maturity, such as the brain and heart. This finding is encouraging for the role of Rg1 in brain recovery after injury.

The Atherva Veda, an ancient sacred Hindu text, has quite a testimony to ginseng's aphrodisiac effects stating: "[the] seed that is poured into the female that forsooth is the way to bring forth a son the strength of the horse, the mule, the goat and the ram, moreover, the strength of the bull (ginseng) bestows on him. This herb will make thee so full of lusty strength that thou shalt, when thou art excited, exhale heat as a thing on fire". Although these stories seem far-fetched and exaggerated, there is truth relating to the powers of ginseng. The beneficial compounds in ginseng elicit an effect on aspects of sex including arousal, desire and performance. This is done through their connection with the release of sex hormones as well as differing effects on the brain and spinal cord, the penis and testes and nitric oxide. Both the American and Asian ginseng affected males by altering the release of hormones but did so in different ways. The Asian ginseng caused higher levels of testosterone, the 'masculinizing' hormone, in the blood while the American type diminished levels of a 'feminizing' hormone known as prolactin. Either way, the balance between these two hormones is altered to a point where testosterone predominates, thus increasing male sexual behaviour. The mechanisms by which these hormones are altered by the ginseng compounds involve a special portion of the brain which connects the nervous system to the endocrine system, via the hypothalamus. The pituitary gland is directly involved in prolactin secretion and has an indirect effect on testosterone secretion through the secretion of a 'connector' hormone that causes testosterone release elsewhere in the body. It is believed that the ginseng compounds directly affect a brain transmitter molecule known as dopamine that is involved in the stimulation of the pituitary gland from the hypothalamus. In addition to its effects on the brain, ginseng also has an effect on nitric oxide (NO). NO is then released from the nerves and enters the bloodstream where it causes relaxation and dilation of blood vessels. This has implicative effects on sexual function in males because the blood vessels in the erectile tissue of the penis obtain more blood allowing for increased erectile function and penetration ability. With as little as 50mg/kg body weight over a three month period, Korean red ginseng that is unpeeled and either steamed or heated can elicit these effects in men. The Korean red ginseng also can have effects on women through the nitric oxide (NO) synthase effect. Increased blood flow to the vaginal tissues due to NO's results in its relaxation resulting in more desirable and pleasurable sexual activity. Other sexual improvements brought about by the increased production of NO are seen in male sperm. Nitric oxide found within the sperm and within the surrounding ejaculate has been shown to increase the sperm's ability to fertilize an egg. This is done through its involvement in aspects including increased mobility and increased general activity in order to help the sperm in the travel to find an egg. Too much NO, however, can be detrimental to the traveling sperm because it also activates the transformation needed to go from the 'traveler-type' sperm to the 'fertilizer-type' sperm through a process known as capacitation. If this occurs too early in the sperm's travels, the sperm would be ready to fertilize but would not be able to reach an egg because of the premature loss of mobility.

So now you are at the end of examinations, things went well and you are happy with your grades. It is hard to say whether the energy drinks laced with ginseng had any effect in such a short time, but having learned much about this plant a new lifestyle may emerge. You have now learned the expense of 1-2 grams of ginseng daily is well worth it, when looking at increased brain function, libido, body health, and sperm fertility. The success encountered during this exam period was well worth its weight in ginseng powder.

Glossary

Acetylcholine: The key chemical in neurons/nerve cells that acts as a neurotransmitter and carrier information across the synaptic cleft (the space between two nerve cells). It is also abbreviated as ACh.

Active Compounds: Part of a compound that has active ingredients.

Adaptogen: A natural herb that helps the body to reduce the effects of stress.

Adrenal Gland: A part of the body that secretes hormones to maintain body functions. It produces adrenaline when the body is under stress.

Adrenaline: The "fight or flight" hormone secreted in the adrenal gland with the purpose of increasing the heart rate and the rate of breathing, among other things so as to encourage action despite fatigue or fear.

Alzheimer's Disease: Progressive form of pre senile dementia, similar to senile dementia however it usually starts in the 40s or 50s; first symptoms are impaired memory which is followed by impaired thought and speech and finally complete helplessness.

Angiogenesis: A physiological process involving the growth of new blood vessels from existing ones.

Anticancer Effects: Used in the prevention or treatment of cancer.

Anti-Inflammatory: Acting to reduce certain signs of inflammation.

Antioxidant: Any substance that stops oxidation.

Aphrodisiac: A substance that arouses sexual desire.

Behavioral Sensitization: As a result of the repeated and escalating application of a stimulus (*i.e.* drugs), the body's response to the stimulus is enhanced and becomes persistent (*i.e.* long term sensitivity to drugs).

Bioavailability: The rate at which a drug or other substance becomes available or absorbed by the body.

Blood- Brain Barrier: A mechanism that prevents blood flow from the circulatory system from reaching the brain.

Bloodstream: Blood circulating through the body.

Central Nervous System: The central nervous system is that part of the nervous system that consists of the brain and spinal cord whereby the brain sends signals through the spinal cord. Both the brain and spinal cord serve as the main "processing center" for the entire nervous system, and control all the workings of the body.

Cerebral Cortex: A tissue in the brain composed of nerve cells that are largely responsible for higher brain functions such as sensation, voluntary muscle movement, thought and reasoning Cholinergic - Nerve cells/fibers that employ acetylcholine as their neurotransmitter, and are stimulated by acetylcholine.

Circulation: Movement of blood in the body through blood vessels that is induced by the pumping of the heart. Circulation distributes oxygen and other nutrients to all tissues.

Dopamine: A neurotransmitter formed in the brain that is essential to the healthy functioning of the central nervous system and has effects on emotion, perception and movement.

Endocrine Gland: Secretes hormones into the blood stream, among other glands, it contains the adrenal gland which secretes adrenaline.

Enzyme: A protein, or protein-based molecule, that speeds up a chemical reaction in a living organism. An enzyme acts as a catalyst for a specific chemical reaction by converting a specific set of reactants called substrates into specific products.

Ejaculate: The process of expelling semen.

Fertilize: The initial step in forming a fetus (baby) from fusion of sperm and egg.

Free Radicals: Atom(s) with an unpaired electron. These are believed to contribute towards aging and cancer.

GABA (gamma-aminobutyric acid): A neurotransmitter which affects nerve cells in the brain by slowing them down.

Gastrointestinal tract: A human's digestive tube.

Genus: A low level taxonomic rank used in the biological classification of living and fossil organisms that is an example of definition by genus and differentia.

Ginko Biloba: Ginkgo (*Ginkgo biloba)* is one of the oldest living tree species and its leaves are among the most extensively studied botanicals in use today. It is used in traditional medicine to treat circulatory disorders and enhance memory. The extract for herbal remedies comes from the leaves and seeds.

Ginsenoside: A compound that is involved in supporting the health-related benefits of Ginseng. They are also steroid glycosides found in the ginseng plant.

Hemolysis: Destruction of red blood cells.

Hippocampus: The part of the brain that regulates emotion, learning, memory encoding and retrieving and spatial orientation.

Hypothalamus: A portion of the brain connected to the pituitary gland.

Inhibit: Prevents something from happening.

Insomnia: Not being able to sleep.

Ischemic Brain Damage: Inadequate blood flow to the brain, either acute (comes and goes) or chronic (long-lasting).

Integrated Sensory-Motor Function: The ability of the brain to process multiple sensory motors into actions thereby making it possible to use our bodies effectively within our environment

Metabolized: Breaking down a substance in the body.

Methamphetamines: A drug used as a stimulant to the nervous system and an appetite suppressant.

Mucosa: A mucus covered membrane that lines the cells in organisms.

Neurotransmitters: A chemical that is released from a nerve cell which thereby transmits an impulse from a nerve cell to another nerve, muscle, organ, or other tissue. A neurotransmitter is a messenger of neurologic information from one cell to another.

Nitric Oxide (NO): A signaling molecule in the body that along with oxygen transportation and transmission of nerve impulses encourages the relaxation and dilation of blood vessels.

Nitric Oxide (NO) Synthase: Enzyme that creates nitric oxide.

Norepinephrine: A hormone secreted in the adrenal gland to assist adrenaline in providing the body with energy in times of stress. It is also a neurotransmitter that passes messages to other neurons.

Northern Hemisphere: Half of the planet that is north of the equator. Hemisphere literally means half sphere. Earth's Northern Hemisphere contains most of its land area and most (about 90%) of its human population.

Palpitations: Rapid, strong, or irregular heartbeat.

Perennial: A plant that lives for more than two years.

Pituitary Gland: Hormone-secreting gland below the brain.

Post- Traumatic Stress Disorder (PTSD): An emotional illness that is classified as an anxiety disorder and usually develops as a result of a terribly frightening, life-threatening, or otherwise highly unsafe experience.

Prolactin: A hormone that diminishes male sex drive and is necessary in women for reproductive functions.

Protein Synthesis: The multi-step process in which cells build proteins.

Psychoactive Stimulants: Drugs that result in habit as a result of their stimulating effect on mood, behaviour, and conscious thought.

Regulatory: Something that maintains balance to a mechanism so it can function.

Rg1, Rb1: Ginsenosides with a depressing effect on the central nervous system. They protect the nervous system from over excitement.

Spatial Orientation: The natural ability to maintain body/physical orientation to the surroundings and natural environment at rest and during motion.

Testosterone: Male sex hormone.

Vasodilation: Widening of blood vessels as a result of the relaxation of the smooth muscle cells in the vessel walls that promote blood flow.

References

Attele, A .S.; Zhou, Y.; Xie, J.; Wu, J. A.; Zhang, L.; Dey, L.; Pugh, W.; Rue, P. A.; Polonsky, K. S.; Yuan, C. 2002. Antidiabetic Effects of Panaz ginseng Berry Extract and the Identification of an Effective Component. Tang Center for Herbal Medicine Research.51, 1851-1858. Retrieved from http://diabetes.diabetesjournals.org/content/51/6/1851.full.pdf+html

Chen, C.; Chiou, W.; and Zhang, J. 2008. Invited Review - Comparison of the pharmacological effects of *Panax ginseng* and *Panax quinquefolium*. *Acta Pharmacologica Sinica*, 29, 1103-1108.

Chen, N. H. 2006. Ginsenoside rb1. Retrieved July 15, 2011 from http://www.imm.ac.cn/download/Chen%20Naihong (Brain%20Research).pdf

Cheng, Y.; Shen, L.; and Zhang, J. 2005. Invited Review - Anti-amnestic and anti-aging effects of ginsenoside Rg1 and Rb1 and its mechanism of action. *Acta Pharmacologica Sinica*, 26(2), 143-149.

Choi, K. 2008. Invited Review - Botanical characteristics, pharmacological effects and medicinal components of Korean *Panax ginseng* C A Meyer. *Acta Pharmacologica Sinica*, 29(9), 1109-1118.

Enviroment Canada. 2010. Information Bulletin - Permit requirements to export American Ginseng from Canada. Retrieved July 16, 2011 from http://www.ec.gc.ca/nature/default.asp?lang=En&n=14AD12F7-1.

Exploration of Ginseng Plantation and Processing. 2009. Sun Ten Quarterly Newsletter. Retrieved July 15, 2011 from http://www.suntenglobal.com/news/img/QNSpring09.pdf

Francis, A.; Chiu-Yin, K. 2003. Nitric oxide, human disease and the herbal products that affect the nitric oxide signalling pathway. *Clinical and Experimental Pharmacology and Physiology*. 30(9). 605-615. DOI: 10.1046/j.1440-1681.2003.03885.x

Friedl, R.; Moeslinger, T.; Kopp, B.; Spieckermann, P. G. 2001. "Stimulation of nitric oxide synthesis by the aqueous extract of Panax ginseng root in RAW 264.7 cells," *British Journal of Pharmacology*, 134, 1663-1670.

Ginseng relaxes blood vessels and lowers blood pressure. 2009. Adaptogens.eu. Retrieved July 15, 2011 from http://adaptogens.eu/ginseng/effects/particular/ginseng-relaxes-blood-vessels-and-lowers-blood-pressure-824.aspx [17/07/2011]

Herrero M. B and Gagnon, C. 2001. Nitric oxide: a novel mediator of sperm function. *Journal of Andrology*. 22, 349-356.

Importance/Function of Proteins. Retrieved July 15, 2011, from http://staff.jccc.net/pdecell/biochemistry/proteins.html#importance

Jia, L.; Zhao, Y.; and Liang, X, J. 2009. Current Evaluation of the Millennium Phytomedicine - Ginseng (II): Collected Chemical Entities, Modern Pharmacology, and Clinical Applications Emanated from Traditional Chinese Medicine. *Current Topics in Medical Chemistry*, 16(22), 2924-2942.

Kevin, B. 2002. Effects of stress and hippocampal nmda. Retrieved July 15, 2011 from http://learnmem.cshlp.org/content/9/2/58.abstract

Kiefer, D; Pantuso, T. 2003. Panax Ginseng, American Association of Family Physicians. Retrieved July 17, 2011 from http://www.aafp.org/afp/2003/1015/p1539.html

Lee, S.; Chu, K.; Sim, J.; Heo, J.; Kim, M. 2008. Ponax Ginseng enhances cognitive performance in Alzheimer disease. Alzheimer Disease & Associated Disorders, 22(3), 222-226. Retrieved July 14, 2011, from the Scholars Portal database.

Life Extension: Health Concerns. 2011. Attention Deficiet/Hyperactivity Disorder. Retrieved July 15, 2011, from http://www.lef.org/protocols/emotional_health/attention_deficit_hyperactivity_01.htm

Liu, L.; Luo, Y.; Zhang, R.; Guo J. 2011. Effects of ginsenosides on hypothalamic-pituitary-adrenal function and brain-derived neurotrophic factor in rats exposed to chronic unpredictable mild stress. *China Journal of Chinese Materia Medica*, 10-25.

Lü, J.; Yao, Q.; Chen, C. 2009. Ginseng Compounds: An Update on their Molecular Mechanisms and Medical Applications. *Current Vascular Pharmacology*, 7(3), 293-302.

Mazza, G.; Cottrell, A.C.; Gao, L. 1996. Ginsenosides in Roots and Leaves of American Ginseng. J.Agric. Food Chem. 44, 717-720. Retrieved July 15, 2011 from http://pubs.acs.org.subzero.lib.uoguelph.ca/doi/pdfplus/10.1021/jf950309f

Pinel, J. P. J. 2009. Biopsychology (7th ed.). Pearson Education, Inc.

PsychCentral. 2011. Anxiety & OCD Exposed: When the Brain Sounds a False Alarm. Retrieved July 16, 2011, from http://blogs.psychcentral.com/anxiety/2009/03/when-the-brain-sounds-a-false-alarm/

Qiao, C.X.; Den, R.; Kudo, K.; Yamada, K.; Takemoto, K.; Wati, H.; and Kanba, S. 2005. Ginseng enhances contextual fear conditioning and neurogenesis in rats. *Neuroscience Research*, 51, 31-38.

Radad, K.; Gille, G.; and Rausch, W.D. 2004. Use of Ginseng in Medicine: Perspectives on CNS Disorders. *Iranian Journal of Pharmacology and Therapeutics*, 3(2), 30-40.

Radad, K.; Gille, G.; Moldzio, R.; Saito, H.; and Rausch, W. D. 2004. Ginsenosides Rb1 and Rg1 effects on mesencephalic dopaminergic cells stressed with glutamate. *Brain Research*, 1021, 41-53.

Sadava, D.; Heller, C.; Orlans, G.; Purves, B.; Hillis, D. (Ed.). 2008. Life: The Sciences of Biology (8th Edition). United States: The Courier Companies Inc.

Sakanaka, M.; Zhu, P.;Tanaka, J.; Kuramoto, M.; Uno, H.; Hatai, R., *et al.* 2007. Intravenous infusion of dihydroginseno side Rb1 prevents compressive spinal cord injury and ischemic brain damage through upregulation of VEGF and Bcl-X-L. *Journal of Neurotrauma*, 24(6), 1037-1054.

Schlag, E. M.; McIntosh, M .S. 2006. Ginsenoside content and variation among and within American ginseng (*Panax quinquefolius* L.) populations. *Phytochemistry* 67, 1510-1519.

Shi, A-W.; Wang, X. B.; Lu, F .X.; Zhu, M. M.; Kong, X. Q.; Cao, K. J. 2011. "Ginsenoside Rg1 promotes endothelial progenitor cell migration and proliferation," *Acta Pharmacol*, Mar; 30 (3): 299-306.

Teeguarden, Ron. 2011. Ginseng - modern knowledge - part 2. Retrieved July 15, 2011 from http://www.ronsblogworld.com/?p=7

The Medical Dictionary. 2011. Psychoactive Stimulants. Retrieved July 16, 2011, from: http://medical-dictionary.thefreedictionary.com/Psychoactive+drugs

Toda, N.; Ayajiki, K.; and Okamura, T. 2005. Nitric oxide and penile erectile function. *Pharmacology & Therapeutics*, 106, 233-266.

U.S. National Library of Medicine National Institutes of Health. 2007. The Role of the Hippocampus on Anxiety-Intracerebral Infusion Studies. Retrieved July 16, 2011, from: http://www.ncbi.nlm.nih.gov/pubmed/17762507

U.S. Public Health Service. Mental Health: A Report of the Surgeon General: Etiology of Anxiety Disorders. Retrieved July 16, 2011, from: http://www.surgeongeneral.gov/library/mentalhealth/chapter4/sec2_1.html

Wong, Cathy. 2010. Health Benefits of American Ginseng. Retrieved July 15, 2011 from http://altmedicine.about.com/od/ginseng/a/american_ginseng.htm

Xiang, Y.Z. Shang, H.C.; Gao, X-M.; and Zhang, B-L. 2008. Review Article - A Comparison of the Ancient Use of Ginseng in Traditional Chinese Medicine with Modern Pharmacological Experiments and Clinical Trials. *Phytotherapy Res*earch, 22, 851-858.

Yue, Patrick *et al.* 2007. Pharmacogenomics and the Yin/Yang actions of ginseng: anti-tumor,angiomodulating and steroid like activities of gensenosides. *Chinese Medicine*. 2(6). DOI:10.1186/1749-8546-2-6.

Zhang, G.; Liu, A.; Zhou, Y; San,X.; Jin, T.; Jin, Y. 2008. *Panax ginseng* ginsenoside-Rg2 protects memory impairment via anti-apoptosis in a rat model with vascular dementia. *Journal of Ethnopharmacology*, 115, 441-448.

Zhang, H.; Zhou, Q.; Li, X.; Zhao, W.; Wang, Y.; Liu, H.; and Li, N. 2007. Ginsenoside Re Promotes Human Sperm Capacitation Through Nitric Oxide-Dependent Pathway. *Molecular Reproduction and Development*, 74, 497–501.

Zhang, H.; Zhou, Q.; Li, X.; Xie, Y.; Duan, X.; Min, F. L.; Liu, B.; Yuan, Z. G. 2006. Ginsenoside R(e) increases fertile and asthenozoospermic infertile human sperm motility by induction of nitric oxide synthase. Archiv der Pharmazie - *Chemistry in Life Sciences Research*, 29, 145–151.

§ 5:

You are invited …

to a

"Flavour-Tripping Party" featuring The Miracle Berries!

As a highly regarded food critic in California, you get an invitation to one of the trendiest dinner parties in Los Angeles. Upon arrival, the Doorman slips you a little package containing some red 'berries'. Seeing your puzzled look, the Doorman is prompted to inform you, "they're perfectly safe and legal, but they will alter your perception." Entering the restaurant, still perplexed by your previous encounter, you nervously pop a few berries into your mouth. Expecting an exciting gastronomic experience, you take a moment to look about. You notice that the Waiters are serving only sour foods and beverages such as sour grapes, gooseberries, lemon sorbet, and radicchio with a vinaigrette dressing. Upon discovering that this is dinner, your stomach turns in revulsion a number of times at the quantity of sour foods. After a sip of San Pellegrino's Limonata, you are completely taken aback by the taste. Eagerly trying more and more foods, a friend stops to warn you, "Overindulgence will leave blisters in your mouth for a few days." But you cannot help yourself; the flavour of the foods has become an exciting adventure! Lemon sorbet tastes sweet, Limonata like lemon sugar water, one bitter radicchio is palatable, and gooseberries no longer make you pucker up. The place is electrified and everyone at the party is raving about this wondrous little taste twister substance, contemplating its legality!

Upon waking up the next morning and eating a fruit for breakfast, you notice that everything tastes normal again. In fact, there are no after effects except for a few blisters in the mouth, a side effect from overdosing on the acidic foods. You begin to wonder what you put in your mouth the previous evening. Willy Wonka himself would have been amazed by this taste bud teaser! The non-descript little red berries that you popped into your mouth have been named 'Miracle Berries' in the West but have been used by the indigenous people of Africa for centuries as a natural flavour modifier of their bitter foods. Originally, the fruit pulp was used to improve the flavour of the maize bread after it had gone sour and to sweeten palm wine.

Without knowing, you have just experienced your first of many flavour-tripping parties. But, was the flavour experience a psychoactive event caused by an unknown natural substance or even an illegal drug deliberately hidden inside a seemingly harmless little red berry?

According to the World Health Organization (WHO) a psychoactive substance is "a substance that, when ingested, affects mental processes, *e.g.* cognition or affect" which do not necessarily lead to psychological dependency, although some certainly do. Powerful and damaging psychoactive substances such as marijuana, cocaine, amphetamines, *etc.* are illegal, but there are also many which are legal such as caffeine, tobacco, alcohol, cleaning fluids, adhesives, some prescription medications, *etc.* Many prescription drugs used to treat various medical conditions, although not prescribed to treat psychiatric conditions, can have psychoactive effects such as changes in perception or behaviour, insomnia, hallucinations or nightmares, as well as taste alterations (gustatory) or chemosensory perception impairment. Alterations in taste are medically referred to as dysgeusia, an altered sense of taste caused by temporary or permanent damage to the taste buds caused by smoking, medical conditions (*e.g.* Parkinson's disease, diabetes, injuries to the mouth, nose or head, *etc.*), medical treatments (chemotherapy and radiation), prescription medications, *etc.*, resulting in metallic, foul tasting, or completely alternate oral taste perceptions. In one medical report, roughly 20-28% of all commonly prescribed drugs (antibiotics, anti-thyroid, heart medications, neurological, zinc preparations) cause dysgeusia or taste perception impairment. For example, agenusia (a form of dysgeusia) refers to the complete loss of at least one of the four taste sensations, *i.e.* salt, sweet, sour and bitter and is often associated with the use of aspirin, inhaled corticosteroids, insulin, or opioids. The second form of dysgeusia depicts an altered perception of taste (but not a complete loss), *i.e.* markedly sweet, bitter, salty or metallic tastes, and is often associated with the use of

Benzocaine or Vitamin D supplements. The third is parageusia, which refers to abnormal or bad taste in the mouth which can be triggered by the use of ACE inhibitors: amoxicillin, decongestants, and the two most common legally available psychoactive drugs, nicotine and alcohol.

Although many substances have demonstrable deleterious impairment of gustatory perception, it is also important to flip the situation around by asking if there are any substances which can improve or amplify gustatory perceptions. In fact, many early research studies have shown that the active cannabinoid tetrahydrocannabinol (abbreviated as THC) in marijuana purportedly improves taste responsiveness while enhancing the sensory appeal of certain foods. Cannabinoids are purported to be responsible for promoting food cravings with various taste properties, most notably sweet foods. In this case, the strengthening of taste pleasure circuits can also explain the reason cannabinoids also promote increased eating behaviour in general. One explanation is that cannabinoids act on the same hedonic brain pleasure circuits that sweet foods activate. Having said this, current research suggests that "nontoxic" agents with taste-enhancing properties may turn out to have a therapeutic value for individuals such as the elderly or other people experiencing diminished appetite and/or quality of life; thus casting some doubts on the total effectiveness of cannabinoids or cannabinoid-like products.

Although the jury may still be out on whether cannabinoids have therapeutic value as general enhancers of taste function, some evidence suggests that the tobacco industry experimented with various natural additives in efforts to improve the chemosensory perception of tobacco smoke. This path was investigated in the hopes to reduce or mask the smoke's harsh taste and irritating properties, thereby promoting deeper inhalation and increased uptake of nicotine along with other harmful substances. In 2004, Wayne and Connoly suggested that the tobacco industry had performed experimental research which showed that the addition of undetectable amounts of menthol flavour (*i.e.* lower the 0.03%) to regular cigarettes caused an "altered [taste] perception of tobacco smoke and its constituents via cooling, smoothing, and anaesthetic effects," thereby reducing nicotine irritation. The R. J. Reynolds' Tobacco Company also explored the use of menthol at below threshold levels in 1985, noting that "subliminal levels of menthol are believed to decrease harshness…" and therefore causes an overall dilution of tobacco sensation received from the smoke and increase nicotine uptake.

If this was not enough, the tobacco industry further explored the use of other natural additives such as peppermint and spearmint oils along with menthol. An early Philip Morris study commented that "Newport delivers a significant amount of peppermint oil into the smoke. This peppermint oil is perceived by the smoker to contribute to the overall cooling effect," thus increasing overall cigarette consumption. Other naturally derived plant additives such as cloves, camphor (a strong aromatic plant substance), and wintergreen all have similar cooling properties and have likewise been considered by some researchers to be substitutes for menthol in cigarettes.

Although it is commonly believed that menthol works mainly on the peripheral nervous system (PNS), its action on the central nervous system (CNS) could have further implications for the addictive nature of tobacco and contribute to the development of dependency. Using R. J. Reynolds' own words, "Menthol is not used for its effects on the central nervous system, however, it can stimulate the central nervous system at all levels. It is considered a brain stem stimulant." This statement indicates that the tobacco industry was completely aware of potential addiction to menthol as well as to the potential of causing other serious CNS disturbances such as confusion, psychosis, and visual disturbances. In the 6th century BC, Confucius wrote,

"Everyone eats and drinks but few appreciate taste". Despite the fact that Confucius wrote this more than millennia ago, his words are still applicable in our modern society. Confucius would have been angry with the tobacco industry using taste modifiers to increase profits while masking the unpleasant taste of a harmful substance. On the other hand, he would have been equally impressed with the taste-manipulating capabilities that we have now come to know and enjoy.

It has been said that the world 'speaks' to us through our senses. Human beings have five physiological senses all of which are equally important. It can easily be argued that the sense of taste (gustation) is most crucial as some foods of early hunter-gatherer societies have become hardwired into our brains. Taste has been used as an indicator of both caloric content and safety, especially considering the scarcity of foods in those times. Based on experience, sweet, salty, and umami tastes are typically understood to be safe to eat while sour and bitter tastes are indicative of food spoilage, food that is not fully ripened, or perhaps even poisonous. At flavour-tripping parties, this hardwiring is fooled as the experience provides a misleading but pleasurable sensation. Here, taste is the sense on the 'hot seat' so to speak. But, how do we actually taste? As with the other four senses, taste is part of the peripheral nervous system, specifically the sensory system, and is a physiological response to an external stimulus. But in order to be experienced, the external stimulus is transmitted through a dedicated organ at the point of 'first contact', in this case, the tongue.

If you've ever taken a look at your tongue through a mirror, you'll notice a soft, reddish brown, velvety looking 'thing' covered with many tiny bumps, looking very much like a shag rug! Not very attractive, but the appearance of the tongue is deceptive and very complex, capable of preforming a variety of simultaneous actions. As well, very tiny bumps called papillae appear in various sizes and shapes with most of the human taste buds being associated with them. The papillae-containing taste buds are, for the most part, located on the tongue with some also under the tongue, inside the cheeks, in the roof of the mouth, on the lips, and in the back of the throat. It is estimated that humans have approximately 10,000 papillae which are replaced every two weeks! Becoming more microscopic, each taste bud contains between 50-100 receptor cells representing each of the five tastes, but many receptor pathways exist for each taste. Each receptor cell membrane has surface protein molecules extending from the outside to the inside of the membrane; it is a trans-membrane receptor protein. These transmembrane receptors are linked to a G-protein (guanine nucleotide-binding proteins) inside the cell which is activated when a specific molecule such as a hormone, neurotransmitter or other molecule bonds to one of the G-protein coupled receptors. The activation of the internal G-protein causes a cascade of intracellular reactions, eventually resulting in the generation of an electrochemical signal (also known as an action potential) which is sent via dedicated nerve fibers. It then travels to higher order processing centers in the brain, and is interpreted as a specific chemoreception response, which results in the subjective experience of taste. The nature of the action potential and the food which generate these responses are learned early in life by association and constant exposure to foods, with some taste preferences being instinctual.

The 'chemical' stimuli received from the 'soup' formed from the chewed food mixed with saliva can cause two different responses. In the first instance, the effect of the bonding molecule causes the admittance of ions into the cell through channels in the membrane, which eventually are interpreted as sour and salty. In the second instance, the binding of a molecule with the G-protein coupled receptor causes an actual change in the 3-D physical structure of the cell membrane leading to the tastes sweet, bitter, or umami. Interestingly, each taste is recognized by its own taste receptor, *i.e.* there is not one universal taste receptor for all food molecules. The miraculin protein works best at a pH 3 level, which is very acidic and does not work at level pH 7 because it is a neutral level equivalent to water. At level pH 6, which is slightly acidic, the protein does have an effect however, the effect is very little.

In most cultures, the desired food tastes are sweet, salty, and umami while sour and bitter are avoided. As evidence for this trend, take another look in your basket the next time you are grocery shopping. The desire for sweet foods is very strong, and subsequently both children and adults will often consume sweet substances in the mid afternoon when they feel tired. Many interesting studies have confirmed that the taste preferences of early humans became hardwired into our brains a long, long time ago. While some may be learned, taste preferences are also innate to human infants who are born with a taste for sweetness, showing preference for sweet sugar solutions rather than their own mother's milk. Many parents can attest to their young child's preference for sweet foods and drinks rather than sour. Bitter and sour tastes are usually the last to be accepted, usually established by the end of the toddler stage as family food taste preferences are learned and reinforced at the family dinner table.

Since the beginning of time, humans have always been on a quest to find foods with a natural sweet taste. Honey is probably the world's oldest sweetener, and can even be observed in a 10,000 year old Spanish cave painting which depicts honey collection. Another ancient sweetener is crystallized sugar from sugar cane (Genus *Saccharum*) which was produced 5,000 years ago in South and Southeast Asia. In fact, even Alexander the Great marvelled at its taste during his Asian expeditions while taking a sample of this 'sacred plant' home. In contrast, Europeans had a very limited selection of sweeteners, despite the introduction of sugar cane by Arabs in the 8th century. Most Europeans would be forced to wait an additional eight long centuries and would not taste the sugar cane's sweetness until long after Christopher Columbus has discovered North and South America. During the 16th century, European colonies were used as a source of sugar production, perhaps to undermine the Arab monopoly. This sugar was an expensive sweet treat reserved only for the upper classes and, ironically, it was partially due to the 19th century Napoleonic wars that sugar from sugar beets (Beta vulgaris L.) made sugar more available and affordable.

While the Miracle Berries consumed at flavour-tripping parties have no detrimental effects, the quest for sweetness has poisoned and killed many unsuspecting people. Compounds such as 'salt of Saturn' (*aka* lead acetate) produced a deceptively sweet taste and it has been hypothesized that the fall of Rome was partially due to lead poisoning. The Emperor Claudius (10 BC-54 AD) had some of the most obvious signs including various neurological, neuromuscular, gastrointestinal, reproductive, and CNS manifestations as well as the common aristocratic Saturnene gout, also caused by lead poisoning. Lead entered Roman cooking through the extensive use of a sweet liquid called Sapa, which was also used in wine preservation, fortification, and sweetening. Pliny the Elder (33-79 AD) wrote that it was prepared by boiling sour wine (which contains high amounts of acetic acid) in lead lined pots, a process which led to the formation of lead acetate. Unknowingly, the attractive sweet flavour of Sapa covered its silent poison and deadly secret. Lead poisoning was, however, known as early as the 5th century BC, when it was described by Hippocrates. Six centuries later, the Greek physician Dioscorides wrote that 'lead causes the mind to give way' while Roman engineers such as Vitruvius preferred to build water pipes out of earthenware, rather than lead.

Sapa was a common wine additive until the 15th century when it was banned in Spanish and French wines, but ingenious wine makers used other sweet, poisonous chemicals such as litharge (lead oxide) instead. Germany went much further than this, by making any wine adulteration punishable by death. Even in the time of Ludwig van Beethoven (1770-1827), lead in wine was still a problem as Ludwig, a heavy wine drinker, had high amounts of lead. Despite these efforts, lead poisoning from foods, wines, ciders, and other hazards (*e.g.* paints) continued to plague Europe and the Americas for many centuries. The presence of lead in wine continued well into the 19th century, contributing to the beginning of food hygiene legislation. In the 20th century, lead still continued to be a silent killer, being added to many everyday products which have since been banned. Lead continues to be a problem, as a 2007 recall of millions of Chinese produced toys had unacceptable lead levels in the paint. While lead's effects are still felt, other heavy toxic metals such as mercury and cadmium have taken its place, accumulating and contaminating many sea animals used for food.

Currently in the 21st century, there is a myriad of available sweetening agents, but the ancient sweet paradox is continued as food and pharmaceutical industries continue their search. Natural sugars are extracted from plant roots, stems, bark, leaves, flowers, seeds, and fruits, as well as from animal sources. Today, the two most popular natural sweeteners are the historical carbohydrate sweeteners - honey and sucrose. The large family of natural sweeteners, however, embrace other carbohydrate (glucose, fructose, dextrose) and non-carbohydrate (glycyrrhizin, sorbitol, stevia, *etc.*) sweeteners. The world of natural sweeteners is highly diverse, and includes unusual substances such as the protein-based sweeteners used by many traditional African foods. Moreover, many modern commercial foods and beverages contain artificial sweeteners which can be produced synthetically by humans. These high intensity sweetening substances have the ability to sweeten products hundreds, if not thousands of times greater than sucrose on a per weight basis. As a result, many of these additives are categorized as low calorie sweeteners, because a lower quantity is required to sweeten foods to the same degree as sugar. Furthermore, the fact that proteins will often lose their activity with heat has caused these sweetening agents to be utilized in non-thermal food and beverage applications. Not satisfied with the caloric density of many natural sweeteners, humans have chemically created a myriad of high intensity artificial sweeteners, many of which can potentially be harmful to humans. An example of an artificial sweetener that can cause detrimental side effects is Aspartame, a chemical which contains two amino acids, aspartic acid and phenylalanine.

While most people can digest it with little difficulty, aspartame is dangerous to people with phenylketonuria because they lack the liver enzyme to metabolize phenylalanine. But can the brain tell the difference between a natural and artificial sweetener? A comparative study between sucrose and artificial sweeteners showed that the latter activated parts of the brain associated with aftertaste much longer than sucrose. This may partially explain the characteristic of artificial sweetening agents, and determine whether they impart a bitter or metallic sensation, especially after long periods of storage. Additionally, the brain makes a distinction between a caloric and a noncaloric sweetener, despite the fact that the conscious mind cannot readily distinguish the two. For instance, the natural ingredient sucrose is distinct from artificial sweeteners, such as sucralose, because it is able to activate the dopaminergic receptors in the midbrain, which are associated with feeling of pleasurable.

The world of flavour modification is indeed peculiar, and there are also chemicals which have the opposite effect of Miracle Berries by weakening the sweetness perception of a food. Furthermore, there are two known high intensity protein sweetness modifiers; however these differ from your ordinary everyday sweeteners. Unlike typical artificial sweeteners, these modifiers only increase the perception of sweetness when the protein is exposed to acidic foods or beverages. One of the two is Miraculin which is a sweet protein contained in the little red berries from a West African evergreen tree called Synsepalum dulcificum. Miraculin, the extract from a miracle berry, is a taste-modifying protein that replaces a sour taste with a sweet taste. The fruit containing this protein is called Richadella Dulcifica, although it is more commonly known as the miracle fruit or the miracle berry. The berry itself is not usually sweet; however, it is the miraculin that changes the flavour. Because it does not have the dangerous side effects that artificial sweeteners contain, it is commonly used as a substitute of artificial sweeteners. With humble beginnings, it is now the star of the cult-like flavour-tripping parties where it is tested by neophytes and experienced tasters alike. For all the excitement the berry offers, it has no claim to being a super food like goji berries. Miraculin is responsible for 10% of the total protein content of the berry which makes this unassuming berry the star of flavour-tripping parties and a blessing to people with impaired taste perception. It has been estimated that one red ripe berry contains 0.04 miligrams of Miraculin which is enough to accomplish its taste switcher abilities. In a single tastant analysis (testing for only one quality in taste), the Miracle Berry showed that sour taste was reduced and replaced by a temporary sweetness. One investigator estimated that a mere 0.02 miligrams of purified Miraculin produces a noticeable increase in the sweetness of lemons coupled with an equally noticeable decrease in sourness.

The miracle berry was first documented nearly three centuries ago in 1725 by the French explorer Chevalier des Marchais during an expedition to West Africa in search of exotic fruits. This search was taken by many cultures to not only improve the palatability of their foods, beverages and medicines, but also to satisfy the insatiable quest for something new and novel by their respective upper classes. During one these journeys, Des Marchais would eat the bland and bitter tasting foods which were quite disagreeable to his 'bourgeoisie' palate, even commenting that the local food was more suitable as a form of religious penance or as a food for prisoners. The very observant Des Marchais noticed that people from Ghana to the Congo picked small elongated red berries, eating them prior to their meals. He believed they could be an appetizer and was therefore disappointed as they had little taste. But to his great delight, he noticed that the unpalatable indigenous foods acquired an unbelievably sweet taste suitable for a king!

Not much was written about Des Marchais's little red 'miracle berry' until an 1852 journal article described its effects. Serious research on the subject did not truly begin until 1968, when Professors L. Beidler and Dr. P. Kuriharist demonstrated that the 'magical properties' of this berry was derived from a protein in the soft flesh of the fruit. This chemical was later called Miraculin by the over-enthusiastic Dutch researchers, who were greatly impressed by its effect on one's palate, or sense of taste. Furthermore, the work by Professor L. Beidler and Dr. P. Kuriharist in 1968 revealed that the sweetness substance in miracle berries is a glycoprotein which is a protein molecule consisting of 191 amino acids (basic building blocks of protein) with a variety of 'sugars' bonded to it. This is essential for its stability and folding properties, but not necessarily for its sweet inducing activities. Twenty years later, researchers identified five different sugars, including the tetradimer and the dimer which account for approximately 14% of the molecule's weight, but they are not present in equal amounts. The tetradimer is made up of four identical subunits and the dimer is made up of two identical subunits; both of these sugars have the ability to modify the taste of a product.

Since the 1960s, there have been numerous attempts to commercialize Miraculin in the United States, but the chemical has received a great deal of opposition from the Food and Drug Administration. In 1973, the offices of the Miralin Company were mysteriously ransacked with the FDA report scattered on the floor. One year later, on the eve of its major launch into the US market, the United States Food and Drug Administration (FDA) unexpectedly classified Miraculin as a food additive, effectively denying its approval for use in the food industry. The investors later subpoenaed the FDA decision, but most of the writing was blacked out. The FDA's decision meant many more years of testing which crushed its launch as investors could not provide further financing. Some people have wondered if other powerful interests played a role in Miraculin's demise. Miraculin has been permitted in Japanese foods since 2006 while other countries have not followed the lead. Despite the regulatory setback, it remains legal to grow and/or sell miracle berries in most countries. To this present day, the FDA's decision remains a puzzle, and the 'office' crime remains unresolved. Another perspective would be for the FDA to re-examine Miraculin with fresh eyes, a renewed heart, and a bowl of miracle berries!

But despite the setbacks, the popularity ofMiracle Berry began to grow through the Internet due to persistent researchers and people with an open mind and curious palates. The berries were used by people experiencing dysgeusia in order to help them to gain weight with fewer dietary restrictions, or 'harsh' medical treatments that can impair or destroy taste buds. People with diabetes have also begun to use miracle berry products to experience sweet flavours without the associated detrimental side effects of elevated blood sugar. Moreover, the rising popularity of mysterious flavour-tripping parties has helped to spread information on miracle berries and their repertoire of decreasing the acidic and sour properties of various food and beverages.

So, how does the Miraculin give the perception of sweetness in acidic conditions? Some evidence from a single tasting analysis showed a slight reduction in taste in saltiness. There are two possible explanations: The first being that the reduction in saltiness may be due to miraculin's interactions with saliva creating a slight sweetness which suppresses saltiness.

Another possible explanation is that the reduction of saltiness could be from miraculin

suppressing sourness of NaCl (NaCl tastes sour via stimulation of sour receptors on the anterior

tongue and circumvallate papillae). It is speculated that miraculin suppresses the sourness from

NaCl, such that we are only able to taste sweetness. The current theory suggests that the

Miraculin molecule acts similarly to molecules which induce sweet, bitter, and umami tastes.

The Miraculin molecule, however, has two bonding sites with both sites bonding to proteins on

the sweet receptor membrane in close proximity to each other. In a binary and trinary tastant

analysis (testing for more than one variable), it was shown that when given a mixture that

contained citric acid (sour taste) and one or two other tastes (bitter and/or salty tastes), sourness

was suppressed and sweetness was enhanced. This proved that the Miracle berry was not only

able to suppress sourness, but also bitterness and/or saltiness. Studies have indicated that sweet-

tasting proteins such as Miraculin interact with specific G-coupled receptors that are different

than the ones which bond low molecular weight sugars. The presence of an acid causes a

conformational change (3-D structural change) in the receptor membrane causing the 'sugar'

molecule on the Miraculin molecule to enter/slip into the sweet receptor site, just like a lock and

key, but Miraculin must be bonded to one specific membrane site. If one of these bonding sites

should 'disengage', the sweet taste would still be perceived which usually remains for a

maximum of two hours. While sweetness is intensified, sourness is still perceived but is not

unpleasant. When the mixture contains citric acid (sour) and a bitter tasting component, a

reduction in bitterness and enhancement in sweetness is measured, but not to the same extent as

sourness and saltiness. The effects of one berry can cause a sweet taste to replace the taste of

sour and bitter foods or drinks for at least fifteen minutes and up to two hours. Miraculin, like other proteins is neutralized by any hot liquid as temperature affects the functioning of all proteins. This can become an issue if used commercially. The pulp must be preserved without heating for the effects of Miraculin to be felt.

Before large-scale commercialization of Miraculin can proceed, a few obstacles have to be overcome just like many plant-based substances. Dr. Theerasilp has found a way to successfully separate miraculin using a solution of sodium chloride. Miraculin by itself has no colour and, when it is added to food, it gives it quite a sweet taste. Miraculin is filtered through a multistep process to make sure that all you have is just the protein miraculin. The first way to separate the protein from the rest of the solution is based on the charge of the molecules in the solution. After this, they filter the new solution and dissolve molecules that are not miraculin. The solution is then separated for a final time by using a gel, which attracts miraculin allowing other molecules to pass through, and what is left is pure miraculin. Along with this process, Japanese and Korean researchers have also done extensive work to produce extractable, stable, and active Miraculin in plants which are easy and inexpensive to grow while bearing much fruit. The protein has been successfully expressed by inserting the Miraculin gene into the DNA of tobacco plants, lettuce, tomatoes, and strawberries. In the tomato, the amount of miraculin protein builds up slowly while the fruit grows and is at its highest amount when the tomato is overripe. When the tomato becomes red in colour, the amount of protein is the highest in the peel, then in the middle layer, the inner layer surrounding the seeds, and finally the seeds themselves. The authors suggest that these miraculin tomatoes could be marketed to people who do not enjoy the acidic taste of tomatoes but still want to obtain their nutritional content.

The genetically produced tomatoes researched in Japan contain just as much miraculin as the miracle berry, and this has led to more research to see if miraculin can be inserted into other field crops. Recombinant production has also been made with the mold *Aspergillus oryzae* and the bacteria *Escherichia coli*, but the latter attempt was not successful as the Miraculin did not have any sugar molecules attached. The attempt with *E. coli* demonstrated that the sugar molecules were not necessary for sweetness activity, a head-scratching discovery. The commercial production of Miraculin took a further step forward in 2010 when transgenic tomatoes produced Miraculin in large amounts in both ripe and overripe tomatoes regardless of gene position in the host DNA or genetic background. There has been a lot of talk about the way producers would like to use these modified tomatoes in the products that they sell. It would be possible to sell these products to those who do not like the original tomato taste. The issue of how to keep the nutritional value of the miraculin tomato when they are put into different products is also being discussed. The shelf-life of the fresh fruit is only 2 to 3 days as Miraculin is destroyed by heating. Freeze-dried pulp is available in granules or in tablets and has a shelf-life of 10 to 18 months.

The story of Miraculin does not end here as there are still many unknowns despite many continuing research investigations. What is known is that Miraculin is safe for human consumption as centuries of use attest. Its ability to 'fool' the human perception of flavour by affecting the taste sensory nervous system makes is a psychoactive substance according to the WHO definition. Miraculin can be very advantageous to an individual's health as it would eliminate a lot of sugar for most foods and drinks. With its ability to make sour substances taste sweet, Miraculin makes healthier food options, with reduced sugar and fat, more appealing. The only disadvantage to adding Miraculin to certain foods is that it would turn what was meant to be a sour food, into a sweet food. Whether or not Miraculin affects the central nervous system, as this is necessary in other definitions of psychoactivity, is for further investigations to unravel.

But it is not an important consideration for flavour trippers who enjoy this mind-blowing experience.

The next time you receive an invitation in the mail, it may just be to an electrifying flavour-tripping party … go, enjoy, experiment, and widen your flavour horizons with this mind-blowing red berry. Eat unusual foods with unusual tastes and decadent low calorie desserts with a small plate of Miracle Berries … you will be pleasantly surprised! But take it easy with the sour foods and the desserts, everything in moderation; and a word of advice; when the FDA or life throws you a lemon, reach for a miracle berry … how sweet it is!

Glossary

ACE inhibitor: A medicine that helps lower blood pressure and decrease the workload on the heart, often given to those with heart disease but can also be used to help treat kidney problems.

Acetic acid: A liquid acid that is the major component of vinegar.

Acidic: The quality of a solution to contain high amounts of Hydrogen molecules making it an acid.

Amino acids: The building blocks of protein, much like pieces of LEGO. There are 20 individual amino acids and every protein is simply a combination of these 20 smaller molecules. About 75 percent of the human body is made up of amino acids and this is why they are so vital to how your system functions.

Amoxicillin: A type of antibiotic, which is an agent used to treat bacterial infections as they destroy or suppress the growth of bacteria.

Artificial sweeteners: A synthetic sugar substitute.

Aspergillus oryzae: Fungus present on most agricultural seeds and often responsible for the spoilage of seeds in bulk storage; also used in the production of fermented food or drink.

Aspartame: An artificial substance used to make something sweeter. It is an artificial substance that does not contain many calories that is added to food or drink to make it taste sweeter.

Brain stem stimulant: Something that stimulates or excites the brainstem which the area at the bottom of the brain that controls many important bodily functions such as breathing.

Benzocaine: A local anesthetic.

Caloric: The quality of providing the body with calories.

Camphor: A strong, fragrant plant substance.

Cannabinoid: A component of marijuana.

Cell: The simplest and most basic unit of all living things.

Central nervous system (CNS): The part of the nervous system consisting of the brain and spinal cord.

Chemoreception response: A response caused by an external chemical stimulation to the senses (*e.g.* the external chemicals in foods are received {by receptors on the cells of the tongue} and processed to create a response - taste).

Chemosensory perception: How a chemical stimulus is perceived or interpreted by the senses. In other words, how a chemical stimulus (*e.g.* food interacting with taste buds) is sensed or recognized (*e.g.* tasted). With chemosensory perception impairment, the ability to recognize a stimulus is disturbed, and therefore one would have impaired taste.

Citric acid: An acidic compound present in all plants and some animal tissues.

Decongestant: A drug used to treat congestion in the nose by reducing inflammation.

DNA-Deoxyribonucleic Acid: The carrier of genetic information. A biological molecule composed of nucleotides that form long chains in combination to create a double helix.

Dysgeusia: An abnormal or impaired sense of taste that may be caused by certain medications or over exposure to certain chemicals which normally leaves a metallic taste within the mouth.

Escherichia coli: Bacteria that is occasionally found in the intestines which as a result may cause food poisoning.

External stimulus: Any type of outside information that is received and processed by the body to result in a reaction or response to that stimulus.

Food additive: A substance added to foods during processing to improve colour, texture, flavour, or keeping qualities; examples are antioxidants, emulsifiers, thickeners, preservatives, and colourants. It is any substance not used in food that is expected to become a component of the food.

G-protein: A responding protein inside of a cell that gets "turned on" when the receptor on the outside of the cell gets stimulated (*e.g.* interacts with a specific molecule). Once "turned on", this protein activates other events within the cell. Think of it as a light switch and a light bulb that are separated by a wall. When the switch on one side of the wall gets flipped (the receptor gets stimulated), it causes the light bulb on the other side of the wall to get turned on (activation of the G protein).

G-protein coupled receptor: A receptor that is coupled (or connected to) a G-protein. When the receptor on the outside of the cell recognizes the stimulus, this then activates the G-protein inside of the cell to initiate a series of events.

Gene: The basic unit capable of transmitting characteristics from one generation to the next. It consists of a specific sequence of DNA or RNA that occupies a fixed position locus on a chromosome.

Glycoprotein: A type of molecule made up of both a carbohydrate (a sugar) and a protein.

Gustatory: Sense of taste.

Hormone: The signalling molecules our bodies use to communicate with our proteins. It is a compound produced from one part of the body, but has an effect on another part of the body (*e.g.* a hormone produced in the brain will affect the bones so that they grow) that regulates many bodily functions.

Inhaled corticosteroids: A type of steroid, often prescribed to individuals with asthma as it reduces inflammation in the lungs and airways to help breathing.

Inhibitor: If switching a light switch on were considered an activator, turning the light switch off would be considered an Inhibitor.

Insulin: A hormone responsible for lowering blood glucose (*i.e.* "blood sugar") to help the body maintain the appropriate blood sugar levels.

Membrane: The outer layer of the cell with many functions, one of which is to contain everything inside the cell and to maintain cell shape.

Microscopic: Very small, can only be seen with a microscope.

Miraculin: A sweetness modifying protein found in the skin of the miracle berry that binds to the taste buds and alters flavour. Makes up 10% of the protein in the berry.

Natural substances: Substances which are prepared from herbs and minerals, not from chemical or synthetic sources.

Natural sugars: Typically refers to those sugars derived from plant material. Sugar from beets, cane or fruit would be natural sugar.

Natural sweeteners: One that has not been altered from how it is found in nature and that actually comes from nature.

Nerve fibers: Long cells in the body that connect from tissues to the brain to keep the brain informed on what the rest of the body is experiencing and also to carry commands from the brain to the rest of the body.

Neurological: Having to do with the nervous system (for example, the nerves and their function, or the brain).

Nicotine: Tobacco products, or the smoking of them (a toxic alkaloid).

Papillae: Very small protrusions or bumps on the tongue.

Parageusia: Bad taste in the mouth.

Peripheral nervous system: The part of the nervous system, outside of the spinal cord and brain, that is responsible for relaying information to and from the central nervous system from other parts of the body

Phenylalanine: Many proteins are converted to a nonessential amino acid, tyrosine, by the body. Too little phenylalanine curbs physical and intellectual growth. Too much phenylalanine, as in phenylketonuria (PKU), is highly toxic to the brain.

Phenylketonuria: A disorder that makes one unable to digest and break down phenylalanine, allowing it to build up in the brain and increase risk of psychological disorders and seizures.

Protein: Compounds found everywhere in living organisms. There are many different proteins that have different and sometimes extremely important functions, many of which are functions inside cells so that the cells are working properly.

Psychoactive substance: A substance that will interfere with mental process if it gets into the system on an individual.

Opioids: A substance that has some characteristics of opiate narcotics (which are addictive drugs that are most often used as painkillers) but does not come from the same substance as opiate narcotics

Receptor: Tiny areas that are found almost anywhere on the body. Receptors recognize a specific stimulus (*e.g.* a food molecule). Once this specific stimulus has been recognized by the receptor, this initiates a series of events for a response to take place, *e.g.* if a food molecule interacts with its specific receptor, this initiates the events responsible for providing a specific taste. There are many different types of receptors such as temperature receptors which recognize changes in temperature to initiate the response of feeling hot or cold, or taste receptors, which would recognize specific food molecules to provide specific tastes.

Receptor cell : A cell responsible for receiving or recognizing information (such as a specific food molecule) so that it can be processed (*e.g.* to generate a taste).

Receptor pathways: Once the information or stimuli has been recognized by receptors, depending on what has been received, a series of specific steps will occur to result in a certain response (in this case, a certain taste).

Recombinant production: This process is a natural process, where a piece of DNA breaks off and joins a different chain of DNA.

Saccharin: A white crystalline compound that is several hundred times sweeter than sugar.

Stimuli: Anything that stimulates or activates a reaction to create a response in the body.

Stimulant: Causes an increase in function

Sucralose: An artificial noncaloric sweetener created from sugar by replacing three hydroxyl groups with three chlorine atoms.

Sucrose: Common table sugar.

Tetrahydocannabinol (THC): The active component in marijuana - meaning the component responsible for the drug's intoxicating effects

Trans-membrane protein: Cells are surrounded by a membrane. Trans-membrane proteins are proteins that sit within this membrane so that they have a portion on the outside of the cell and a portion on the inside on the cell.

Trans-membrane receptors: Receptors that go through the membrane *i.e.* has a portion of the receptor on the outside of the cell and a portion of the receptor on the inside of the cell.

References

Capitanio, A.; Lucci, G.; and Tommasi, L. 2011. Mixing Taste Illusions: The Effect of Miraculin on Binary and Trinary Mixtures. *Journal of Sensory Studies,* 26, 54-61.

Giudice, M. 2006. Taste disturbances linked to drug use, CPO/RPC, 139(2), 70-73.

Hirai, T.; Sato, M.; Toyooka, M.; Sun, H-J.; Yano, M.; and Ezura, H. 2010. Miraculin, a taste-modifying protein is secreted into intercellular spaces in plant cells. *Journal of Plant Physiology*, 167, 209-215.

Inglett, G. E. 1976. A history of sweeteners-natural and synthetic. *Journal of Toxicology and Environmental Health*, Part A, 2(1), 207-214.

Joanna, S. 2007. "To Make Lemons Into Lemonade, Try 'Miracle Fruit". Wall Street Journal. http://online.wsj.com/article_email/SB117522147769754148lMyQjAxMDE3NzM1MDIzMjAx Wj.html. Retrieved 2008-05-28.

Kim, Y. W.; Kato, K. K.; Hirai, T.; Hiwasa-Tanase, K.; and Ezura, H. 2010. Spatial and Developmental Profiling of Miraculin Accumulation in Transgenic Tomato Fruits Expressing the Miraculin Gene Constitutively. *Journal of Agricultural and Food Chemistry*, 58, 282-286.
Kurihara, K. and Beidler, L. M. 1969. Mechanism of the Action of Taste-modifying Protein. *Nature*, 222, 1176-1179.

Mattes, R. D.; Shaw, L. M. and Engelman, K. 1994. Effects of Cannabinoids (Marijuana) on taste intensity and hedonic ratings and salivary flow of adults. *Chemical Sense*, 19(2), 125-140.

Paladino, A.; Colonna, G.; Facchiano, A. M.; Constantini, S. 2010. Functional hypothesis on miraculin' sweetness by a molecular dynamics approach. *Biochemical and Biophysical Research Communications*, 396(3), 726-730.

Riera, C. E.; Vogel, H.; Simon, S. A. and le Coutre1, J. 2007. Artificial sweeteners and salts producing a metallic taste sensation activate TRPV1 receptors. *American Journal of Physiology-Regulatory, Integrative and Comparative Physiology*, 293, R626-R634.

Schiffman, S .S. 1991. Drugs influencing taste and smell perception. In: T. V. Getchell, L. M. Doty, B. R. L.; and Snow, J. B. (editors), Smell and taste in Health and Disease.

Sun, H- J.; Kataoka, H.; Yano, M.; and Ezura, H. 2007. Genetically stable expression of functional Miraculin, a new type of alternative sweetener, in transgenic tomato plants. *Plant Biotechnology Journal*, 5, 768-777.

Theerasilp S.; Kurihara Y. 1988. Complete purification and characterization of the taste-modifying protein, Miraculin, from miracle fruit. *Journal of Biological Chemistry*, 263 (23), 11536–11539.

Wayne, G .F.; and Connolly, G. N. 2004. Application, function and effects of menthol in cigarettes: *A Survey of Tobacco Industry Documents Nicotine & Tobacco Research*, 6(S1), 843-854.

§6:

"Nutmeg-nificent?"

Mankind has long had an insatiable curiosity and thirst to have an 'out of this world', or 'mind bending' experience. People have tried almost every imaginable substance under the sun in order to achieve this altered state of mind in an attempt to communicate with divine spirits, or to expand their own consciousness. Every plant, animal, and other non-organic substance has been tried whether it be a natural substance like spider webs or man-made such as LSD. Nearly every avenue of ingestion has been explored in order to achieve an altered state of consciousness. To satisfy this seemingly urgent need, substances have been smoked, consumed, injected, inhaled, or applied topically. While some substances have the desirable psychoactive effects, those of Sea Bream intoxication are quite dramatic and extreme. Most people, however, don't realize that there are ingredients in their own kitchen pantries that can give them their desired 'buzz'.

It is 5 p.m., and it is already dark. The snow is flying, a cold wind is blowing from the north, and people are rushing to get into a warm place. It's Christmas time, and once again the minds of many turn to celebrating this joyous season by gathering with family, friends, and colleagues around tables heavily burdened with copious amounts of rich foods and beverages. Having received an invitation to a neighbourhood get together, you decide to bring a bowlful of grandma's traditional eggnog recipe which is full of all the 'good' things: cream, eggs, bourbon, brandy, and generous amounts of nutmeg. Looking for grandma's heirloom recipe, you find it but the writing is barely legible. Despite this obstacle, you persevere having made it many times before.

The day of the neighbourhood celebration finally arrives and you proudly bring gran's eggnog to the festivities. During the course of the evening, everyone at the party is enjoying the concoction. Sitting by the fire place sipping the nog, you start to feel a little nauseous and have

cramps but make no overtones of it to anyone as you think it might just be a touch of the flu and

the hectic pace of the season. Soon, the nausea turns into an overly joyful feeling, a bit of

euphoria. Thinking that it is the alcohol, you take another generous cupful. Looking at the nog,

there are perhaps just too many little nutmeg specks but you discount your observation thinking

that your mind is playing a trick on you ... it must be the alcohol. After a few hours, you have

more of the warm fuzzies but also start to experience a few additional mental and physical

symptoms that cannot be blamed on either the flu or the alcohol. Drinking more fluids does not

help either, so you go home feeling somewhat better during the night but as the early morning

dawns, you once again feel the same sensation as the evening before. Without knowing it, these

symptoms were not caused by any illness or by the alcohol; it was caused by the more than

generous dose of nutmeg in the nog due to the inability to read gran's recipe clearly.

A spice that is quite common in most kitchen pantries, that has been used throughout both

Eastern and Western culinary history caused the unexpected 'high'. The nutty, warm, and

slightly sweet nutmeg spice is produced from the seeds of the nutmeg tree (*Myristica fragrans*),

an evergreen tree indigenous to the Banda Islands in the Moluccas (Indonesia), and otherwise

known as the "Spice Islands". Producing a fruit called a drupe, just like a peach or cherry, it is

the only tropical tree known to produce two spices; nutmeg which is the actual seed of the tree

and its sister spice mace, the dried net-like covering of the nutmeg seed. Most Westerners only

use powdered nutmeg and mace for flavour in foods, while being completely oblivious to any of

nutmeg's other contributions. If consumed in large enough quantities, nutmeg can have

powerful psychoactive and physiological effects. The high induced by a nutmeg overdose may

cause uncomfortable physical symptoms but is rarely fatal. While its effects on the central nervous system (CNS) or the brain are more similar to those of marijuana or other deliriant or hallucinogenic drugs, it is the physical effects, which can remain for up to three days, that seem to discourage most people from using nutmeg recreationally to get a 'high' or a 'buzz.' Among recreational drug users, nutmeg is not known as a gentle drug and its effects are considered to be the least enjoyable of all drugs.

Throughout history, spices have added much flavour to stale foods and wines as well as being used as food preservatives. These exotic spices were also used for perfumes, incense, and medicine and were gifts suitable only for the rich and powerful. Spices too had unusual uses including the payment of ransoms such as the 1.5 tonnes of pepper paid to the invading Visigoths to end their siege on Rome in 408 A.D. Pepper was used as a bargaining chip because of its use as a preservative and its ability to "mask the appetite-killing stench of decay." Indeed, the history of spices is an intriguing and fascinating slice of food history written in blood as the quest to control the spice monopoly sparked many wars between European nations. Notably, this quest to control spices sparked the colonisation of land all around the world where countries had the intention of exploiting as much of the resources available in order to gain more diverse bargaining chips. For example, the Dutch had an interest in the Molucca islands, mostly due to the nutmeg and other tree spices in that area. By the late 1600's, the Dutch controlled the monopoly over the growth of nutmeg in the Molucca islands, and surrounding areas. To ensure control over nutmeg, the Dutch had destroyed nutmeg trees on the Ternate and Tidore Islands, both parts of the Molucca Islands. The Dutch then used the island of Ambon, an island on which they had a strong control, for the development of nutmeg plantations. Indeed, the discovery of spices while thought of in romantic terms is quite the opposite. The quest for spices was indeed a 'spicy' adventure as the long sea journeys were perilous with ships battered by weather, waves, and pirates, all for a small quantity of spices. Indigenous people were the greatest losers, not only losing the control of their lands but also suffering greatly as they were enslaved and exposed to many new illnesses while working under harsh conditions. For example, the Dutch had control over most of the Molucca Islands and they took control over the Archipelago's most lucrative exports while the commercial centers of cosmopolitan life were either destroyed or declined through loss of their vital trade. Nutmeg has been very important as a spice and commodity for years to the Molucca province of Indonesia. These islands attracted explorers from all over the world who wanted to find and trade the spices found only there, such as nutmeg. The desire to have exclusive control over this lucrative and exotic spice unexpectedly brought about other events including sparking Europe's Great Age of Exploration during the 1400-1600s. It was the drive to be the first to find the route to India which lead to the discovery of North, Central, and South America as well as the Caribbean islands. The Banda islands of the Molucca province were only about 40 square miles wide but they were a crucial destination for countries who wanted to exploit and sell the spices. Likewise, it lead to a monopoly of nutmeg trade and provided a geographical dominance in the area.

With its origins in The Spice Islands, the evergreen nutmeg tree whose fruit yields both nutmeg and its sister spice mace, had been used extensively in the East for thousands of years. In the West, however, nutmeg and mace were not known until the first century A.D. At this time, Pliny the Elder, a Roman author and naturalist who during his investigation into the unreasonably high pepper prices, learned about a tree bearing nuts with two flavours. But being transported overland in caravans, the journey itself was strenuous. It was full of dangers and hardships as the caravans traveled through harsh environments and violent oceans, all the while having to fight off many bandits and pirates along the way. During these journeys, the spices were transferred to a variety of owners many times, and with each transfer the price also increased. So, to a degree it was understandable that pepper from India was expensive but Pliny thought it was just way over the top. Beyond Pliny's brief reference, however, there are no other references to nutmeg in the first five hundred years of European writing.

In the 6th century A.D., nutmeg was brought by Arab merchants from the Moluccas to Constantinople, the location of their source coded in the phrase "fifteen day's sail east from the Island of Java." It was not until 1512, in the West when the Portuguese found nutmeg growing in the Banda, the largest of the Molucca spice islands of Indonesia, that the exact origin of nutmeg was determined. Conquering Constantinople in 641 A.D., the Ottoman Turks shut down the overland spice route between Rome and India, arm wrestling Europe into dealing with them on their terms. Nutmeg was so rare and expensive that it was known in Europe by the end of the 12th century. It is presumed that before Emperor Henry VI of England entered Rome in 1191, the streets were fumigated with nutmeg and other aromatic herbs before coronation by Pope Celestine III. Through the daring exploratory skills of Arab navigators and the rich and powerful trading Venetian seaport with its intelligent merchants, Europe received many new and intriguing foods and spices such as coffee, nutmeg, saffron, cloves, and cinnamon. In the 13th century, Europe basked in the victorious fragrance of spices as the Crusaders brought back unusual spices from the Middle East as spoils of war. In 14th century Europe, a measly 500 grams of nutmeg had cost either three sheep or one cow, whereas the same amount of ginger had only cost one sheep. In addition, the same amount of cloves cost an astonishing seven sheep. With prices like these, spices were out of reach for the commoner, even in times of sickness. During the outbreak of the Plague, the price of nutmeg sky rocketed as it was believed to be effective against it, costing as much as seven fat oxen in Germany for 500 grams.

The race to find the shortest route to the East Indies was fierce and extremely competitive, costing many human lives. Over half of the groups of explorers never returned home. Sailing westwards on behalf of the Spanish Crown in 1492, Christopher Columbus was looking for the shortest route to the Indies, and nutmeg was a must find for him. Columbus did not, however, make it to the Indies nor did he find nutmeg. The quest for spices continued to heat up to the point that it warranted the intervention of Pope Alexander VI who helped negotiate the Treaty of Tordesillas in 1494. This peace treaty successfully settled the long heated and violent dispute between the Catholic countries of Portugal and Spain. This finally brought calm to Europe as these two nations had been at each other's throats. The two countries agreed on a line of separation with Spain taking everything to the west, and Portugal taking everything to the east. This truce line in the sea, however, was not always recognized by either nation.

Wasting no time, the Portuguese sent Vasco da Gama eastward to find the route to India, and he did not disappoint. In 1497, he sailed around the Cape of Good Hope on the southern tip of Africa and was greeted by the Indian Ocean. He had smooth sailing to Calicut on the southern tip of India. da Gama returned to Portugal, nearly two years later, with ships loaded with spices.[4] His arrival was announced from far away as the ocean breeze carried the fragrances from his ship inland. da Gama became a hero as he had opened up a gateway to the spices of the East. This was in great contrast to Columbus who was regarded as a failure in Spain. da Gama's naval equipment, maps, and diaries were so valuable that they were locked up and kept under close guard. To say the least, the Ottomans and the Venetians were completely stunned, and da Gama's discovery decisively broke up their iron grip on the spice trade in Europe. But this was not the end of spice monopolies as other European nations soon took their place.

The Arabs had only been in the Molucca Islands (center for the Asian spice trade) for 30 years when the Portuguese Vasco da Gama landed on its shores in 1512, subsequently wrestling the islands and the spices out of Arab hands. The news eventually reached Europe, setting off a virtual firestorm of exploratory activity in Europe. Both Jacques Cartier (sailing for France in 1535) and Henry Hudson (sailing for England in 1607 and The Netherlands in 1609) set westward looking for the Northwest Passage, a shortcut to the East where precious nutmeg and other spices lay. In a short amount of time, however, both Spain and Portugal were at each other's throats once again in a violent dispute over who owned the Molucca Islands. "The Treaty of Zarogoza" was signed on April 22, 1529 between King John the III of Portugal and Emperor Charles V of Spain. It temporarily succeeded in laying out the role each country was to play in Asia. This Treaty brought peace once again by resolving the Moluccas issue. Eventually the Moluccas Islands became Portuguese but only after Portugal had paid Spain a very sizeable amount of cold hard gold. In the 17th-18th centuries other European countries continued to fight many bloody wars amongst themselves but in 1602, the Dutch gained the upper hand on the "Spice Islands", making them a part of the Dutch East Indies Empire. So tight was their control of the spices that to prevent the spreading of their precious spice plants through bird droppings, the Dutch sent out search and destroy missions spending much effort to wipe out the birds, even going as far as to burn sprouting plants on nearby islands. In time, however, the French were able to smuggle nutmeg seeds to its own colonies effectively breaking the Dutch monopoly. In 1796, the British, gained control ending the Dutch dominance of the Molucca Islands.

In Indian, Arabic and European cultures, nutmeg was never prescribed for its psychoactive effects. Although the acute psychosis and narcotic effects of nutmeg intoxication were known, the number of documented cases in historical, medical or toxicological literature is few. Sixteenth century Europe knew nutmeg to have psychoactive properties including anti-depressive, anxiogenic (a substance causing anxiety) as well as inducing both visual and tactile hallucinations. Nutmeg psychoactivity was observed more as a consequence of its administration for a primary medical condition rather than for recreational drug use. It was quite by accident that the psychoactive properties of nutmeg were observed more in women than men in 18th and 19th century England as women took large doses to induce abortions. The use of nutmeg as a psychoactive drug seemed to go under the radar screen resurfacing in the 1940s in the prisons of the United States. In his autobiography, the infamous Malcolm X writes that while incarcerated in 1946 in a Charlestown prison before his conversion to Islam, he purchased penny matchboxes filled with nutmeg from the kitchen worker inmates. As his smuggled supplies of marijuana were intercepted and he craved the 'high', Malcolm used nutmeg instead, emptying a matchbox full of nutmeg into a glass of water and drinking the concoction. Just one of these matchboxes as enough to give him the same kick as three to four marijuana cigarettes. While he enjoyed the 'high' that he so craved, it had physical side effects, which he did not enjoy at all. These effects come from the anti-depressant, anxiogenic, and hallucinogenic properties of the chemicals. The prison guards eventually caught on and banned nutmeg from the prison kitchen. Still to this day, people are experimenting with nutmeg but the number of known cases of nutmeg intoxication is small and the number of reported cases even smaller. A growth in the use of nutmeg as a drug occurred in 2010 when an increasing amount of people in Florida became ill due to ingesting or smoking nutmeg spice. The cases unfortunately tend to involve teenagers who are novices in experimenting with mind altering substances, some under the impression that nutmeg contains THC, the active psychoactive substance in marijuana. This should come as no big surprise as teenagers are unfortunately known to try many different things in order to get high including smoking grape leaves. Being legal, relatively inexpensive, and readily available at the corner store or supermarket, it is a choice that is often made.

The effects of consuming excessive amounts of nutmeg vary. Symptoms, such as nervousness, fear, feeling of impending doom, tingling around the mouth, tremors, dizziness, blurred vision, agitation and hallucinations reflect nutmeg's ability to stimulate the central nervous system. Nutmeg also inhibits acetylcholine, a chemical referred to as a neurotransmitter. Although acetylcholine is part of both the central nervous system (CNS) and the peripheral nervous system (all nerves that are not included in the brain and spinal cord), nutmeg's effects on acetylcholine is most documented in the peripheral nervous system (PNS). Acetylcholine is responsible for activating muscle cells resulting in movement. Thus when the neurotransmitter is inhibited, movement and coordination are decreased. As a result, nutmeg has been used in Asia since The Middle Ages to stop muscle spasms and diarrhea.

Nutmeg can be broken down into two different oils: fixed oils (nutmeg butter) and aromatic oil (pale-yellow liquid with distinct spice odour). The major components in aromatic nutmeg oil are responsible for both the CNS and physiological effects. They appear to be myristicin, elemicin, safrole, and trimyristin, the four accounting for 85%-95% of the oil's content. Myristicin only accounts for a small 4-12% depending upon its origin and is structurally similar to mescaline. This suggests that it is a serotonin agonist, a chemical which binds to receptors on cell surfaces causing a response similar to that of the natural substance serotonin (a chemical in the brain that is thought to regulate "mood, emotion, sleep and appetite").

Currently, no clinical investigations have been conducted to determine the therapeutic or intoxicating dosing levels of nutmeg. Information about nutmeg intoxication can only be glanced at from the occasional reports in either medical or toxicological literature. Taken orally, either in beverages or by swallowing a large number of nutmeg filled gel capsules, doses of 1 to 3 whole nutmeg kernels are required for a psychoactive effect. Overdoses, however, have been known to occur with as little as 1 whole nutmeg kernel providing 1-2 mg of myristicin per kilogram of body weight. In 1998, Rudgley estimated that a person had to orally consume 6 teaspoons of nutmeg to induce CNS effects. A literature analysis conducted by Ibo Nagano in 2009, however, suggested that only 1 to 1.5 teaspoons of nutmeg is required to experience euphoria, relaxation, mood elevation and an enhancement of the senses. Consuming higher doses such as 1.5 to 3 tsp (6 to 10 grams) of nutmeg causes an individual to enter a dream-like state, have sluggish speech and a moderate loss of coordination. Higher doses of nutmeg significantly affect the CNS by causing an increase in heart rate, severe loss of coordination and difficulty breathing. The effect of dosing differs from one person to another. In one small study, 10 people were given 400 mg of myristicin. Four of the 10 people experienced psychoactive effects. Researchers concluded that 400 mg was the "threshold effective dose" for almost half of the population. The results of this study is consistent with Rudgley's earlier findings where he claimed that a person must consume a minimum of 3 to 5 grams of nutmeg to experience the early stages of psychoactive activities caused by nutmeg. Based on the contents of nutmeg, analysis has shown that myristicin makes up only about 1.3% of the nutmeg weight and only 4-8% of nutmeg's aromatic oil. Since 400 mg of myristicin is twice the dose needed to cause moderate psychoactive effects in humans, it appears that myristicin is not the only psychoactive substance in nutmeg.

The toxic effects of nutmeg have been studied in rats and have shown no life threatening symptoms. Further, tests on people suffering from nutmeg poisoning have shown that the consumption of excess amounts of nutmeg has no life threatening effects. The Journal of

Internal Medicine reported the case of a thirty-two-year-old man who sought emergency room care after ingesting 7 grams of ground nutmeg. The hospital performed tests on the man and found that his blood count, electrolyte levels, calcium and liver enzymes were all within normal range. Furthermore, the Journal of Clinical Toxicology reported on a nutmeg poisoning case involving a thirteen-year-old boy who had ingested 15-25 grams of nutmeg. Tests conducted showed that his electrolyte levels, kidney and liver function, urinalysis, blood, and a pelvic ultrasound all returned without abnormality.

Myristicin has demonstrated no carcinogenic properties. The safrole constituent however, is regarded as a weak carcinogenic agent in rats by the United States government. Due to its critical role in the manufacture of Ecstasy, it is listed as a substance of interest on the United States Drug Enforcement Agency as well as in legislation of The European Union, and as a drug precursor in the United Nations Convention against Illicit Traffic in Narcotic Drugs and Psychotropic Substances.

Along with myristicin, elemicin in the nutmeg extract has been shown to have psychoactive effects, albeit different. Myristicin affects the enzyme monoamine oxidase, whereas elemicin affects nerve cells affected by dopamine. Many studies have shown that myristicin is a weak monoamine oxidase inhibitor (MAOI) in the CNS, a group of antidepressant drugs used as a last resort by people working in mental health, and its hallucinogenic effects probably being a side effect. MAOIs prevent the enzymatic breakdown of the monoamine neurotransmitters serotonin and dopamine which are known as the natural 'happy pill' and the 'reward or pleasure drug'. In view of myristicin's lack of activity in the peripheral nervous system (PNS), it is probable that it is able to cross the blood-brain barrier, therefore making its way to the brain and concentrating its effects there.

Myristicin has been shown to increase the amounts of serotonin in the brain by blocking the release of serotonin into the synapse (*i.e.* the space between adjacent nerve cells, thereby affecting its anti-depressant effects). The build-up of unreleased and unused serotonin in the nerve cells, however, can produce euphoric and hallucinogenic experiences as one of the prime functions of serotonin is to regulate mood. This would explain the historical accounts of euphoria. In the 1970s some studies suggested that myristicin was metabolized into psychoactive amphetamine derivatives (*e.g.* Ecstasy) which increase the levels of all four amine neurotransmitters, including serotonin and dopamine in the brain. This biological metabolic pathway was demonstrated in 1997. The products of the amphetamine breakdown such as tertiary amniopropiophenones have been identified from urine of rats and guinea pigs given myristicin. These metabolites were excreted in the urine and are products of the pathway. It could be that myristicin, however, is metabolized into compounds which could have similar effects as amphetamines as both nutmeg and amphetamines. Although myristicin is the agent which leads to nutmeg intoxication, it is believed that other substances in the aromatic nutmeg oil are also responsible. Myristicin and elemicin are structurally similar to the hallucinogen, mescaline. In a 1978 study, both myristicin and elemicin were administered orally to rodents. The rodents experienced impaired co-ordination and decreased motor activity, which confirmed the 1973 work of Cesario de Mello and Carlini. In 2009, researchers used an animal seizure model to study whether nutmeg oil could be used as an anticonvulsant treatment due to its ability to decrease motor activity. Nutmeg oil was tested to evaluate the potential for acute toxicity and acute neurotoxicity. At low doses, nutmeg oil showed significant anticonvulsant effects against pentylenetetrazole induced seizures, but a weak response at higher doses. This suggests that nutmeg oil may be an effective treatment for seizures in humans.

The CNS excitation effects of nutmeg can be either pleasurable or accompanied with anxiety or fear as the psychological context has a great influence on the effect. Hysterical laughter, cognitive function, semi-consciousness and visual and tactile hallucinations occur at the peak of the intoxication. In fact, it has been found that nutmeg has similar characteristics to a combination of alcohol and marijuana. The physical effects of nutmeg intoxication include outbreaks of sweat, warming of the limbs, headaches, extreme nausea and vomiting, dry mouth, increased heart rate, skin flushing, difficulty urinating, and temporary constipation with symptoms beginning to appear from 0.5-8 hours following its consumption. The recovery phase, like the excitation phase, can be marked by the same physical side effects with some lingering for as long as 24-72 hours.

More specifically, the physical effects of nutmeg can be broken down into six distinct stages:

1. Threshold stage (1-4 hours)
Includes only mild effects, such as feeling energetic and relaxed at the same time, as well as a minor headaches or feeling lightheaded.

2. Initial inebriation (4-8 hours)
The individual may be in a dream-like state, in which they are likely to experience time distortion, "enhanced" senses, and slurred speech.

3. Peak inebriation (8-12 hours)
The effects are at their greatest – includes hallucinations, disturbance in peripheral vision, closed eye visuals, slurred speech, and a loss of coordination.

4. End of peak (13-18 hours)
The effects experienced during the peak inebriation stage (stage 3) slowly decrease in waves.

5. Residual inebriation (19-25 hours)
The main effects have begun to wear off; the individual may feel tired or weak.

6. Final stage (26-32 hours)
The individual returns back to baseline; Normalization continues and a disturbance in concentration may persist for a day or two.

The method of nutmeg extract administration seems to have differing effects as demonstrated by El-Alfy in 2009. Using mice, El-Alfy showed that the mice which had the extract injected into their bellies experienced CNS depression resulting in euphoria whereas those who consumed the same dose orally experienced CNS stimulation, hallucinations, blurred vision, nausea, and paranoia.

Nutmeg has been and continues to be used for its many different medicinal benefits. The Indian, Chinese and Arabic cultures have been using nutmeg for thousands of years. At various times throughout history nutmeg has been used as an anticonvulsant, to control inflammation and clot formation, as a pain reliever possibly in rheumatoid arthritis, a digestive and calming aid, and as a stimulant. Anticonvulsant effects have a quick onset after administration but the effects depend on the dosage. Traditional folk medicine has also used nutmeg as a male aphrodisiac which is applied topically to treat male erectile dysfunctions. The part of the aromatic nutmeg oil that contains eugenol may be responsible for the aphrodisiac effect as it relaxes and dilates blood vessels as well as relaxing smooth muscle. This historical use is supported by 16th century advice from monks who counselled young men to rub nutmeg on their genital area to strengthen their virility. A 2005 study with male rats showed that an extract of nutmeg increased both the libido and potency in male rats but the extract was consumed orally, not applied topically. For women, nutmeg has been 'prescribed' to induce abortions as well as for inducing the menstrual cycle but none of these have been substantiated by any scientific investigations.

Nutmeg has been used for a variety of purposes in both Asia and Europe ranging from food to medicine to perfume. The uses of nutmeg were often shrouded in mysticism and superstition. Some of the purported medicinal uses have been substantiated while others have been proven to be untrue or are still waiting to be tested. Nutmeg and other fragrant herbs were once considered the only appropriate gifts fit for a king, much like a rare wine or exotic perfume. It is a great irony then that nutmeg, once used by only the rich and powerful is now the domain of the commoner. In a nutshell, the nutmeg story is a spicy adventure, and its psychoactive properties will indeed give the user a return ticket for the trip of a lifetime!

Glossary

Acetylcholine: A compound that occurs throughout the nervous system and functions as a chemical neurotransmitter. It is secreted at the ending of nerve fibres and is key in enabling muscles to move.

Agonist: A substance that initiates a response from the body.

Amniopropiophenone: An antidote for cyanide poisoning.

Amphetamine: A substance that increases energy and wakefulness, as well as decreasing appetite and fatigue.

Anticonvulsant: Any drug or substance that prevents or stops the occurrence of seizures.

Antidepressant: Medication used to treat or prevent depression.

Anxiogenic: A substance that creates anxiety symptoms.

Aphrodisiac: Something (person, place, thing, etc), that causes sexual excitement, desire and arousal.

Archipelago: A group of islands.

Aromatic: A substance or plant producing a gratifying and distinctive smell.

Blood-brain barrier: A barrier created from a network of capillaries covering the outside layer of the brain. This barrier prevents toxic substances from transferring out of the blood and crossing over and into brain tissues.

Calcium: A micronutrient; mineral. Many physiological processes involve calcium ions.

Carcinogenic: A substance that can cause cancer.

Central Nervous System (CNS): The part of the nervous system that contains the brain and spinal cord in vertebrates. Impulses from this system travel away from the brain and spinal cord and monitor and coordinate motor activity of the whole nervous system.

Cognition: The process or act of knowing something; a thought.

Constantinople: The capital of the Eastern Roman Empire, the Latin and Ottoman Empires; the former name of Instanbul from 330 A.D. to the 20th century.

Cow: A form of currency used. The unit "Cow" is worth more than sheep but less than oxen.

CNS: *Cf.* central nervous system.

Deliriant: A substance that causes hallucinations by blocking the actions of acetylcholine.

Dopamine: A neurotransmitter responsible for feelings of pleasure and reward. Also a precursor for other substances such as adrenalin.

Drupe: A fruit that contains nutmeg and mace.

Dutch East Indies Empire: An area in Asia that is now part of Indonesia but was a Dutch colony from 1800 to 1963.

Electrolytes: Substances that dissociate into ions when placed into solution, allowing for the conduction of electrical currents.

Elemicin: An organic compound - specifically a phenylpropene that is a part of the aromatic oil in nutmeg; one of the substances found in nutmeg responsible for its psychoactive effects.

Eugenol: A substance found in aromatic nutmeg oil responsible for relaxing muscles and dilating blood vessels.

Euphoria: A feeling of extreme happiness, well-being, and confidence; a manic feeling.

Evergreen: A plant that keeps its leaves year round.

Hallucinogenic: A substance that induces hallucinations (hallucinations are altered perceptions of reality, not to be confused with delusions).

Hematology: The study of the etiology, pathology and functioning of blood, blood disease, and blood-forming organs.

MAOI: *Cf,* monoamine oxidase inhibitor.

Mescaline: A substance found in the peyote cactus that has intoxicating and hallucinogenic effects.

Metabolic pathway: A sequence of chemical reactions undergone by a compound in a living organism.

Metabolites: Products of metabolism.

Molucca Islands: A cluster of islands that is part of Indonesia.

Monoamine Oxidase Inhibitor (MAOI): A group of anti-depressant drugs that inhibits the activity of monoamine oxidase.

Monoamine Oxidase: An enzyme present in most tissues that catalyzes the oxidation (combining with oxygen) and inactivation of monoamine neurotransmitters.

Myristica fragrans: The Latin name for the evergreen tree that produces the nutmeg seed.

Myristicin: A phenolic ether that is responsible for the strong scent present in nutmeg oil, (the essential oil from nutmeg).

Narcotic: A substance or drug that affects behaviour or mood.

Nervous system: A network of cells and fibers that transmits nerve impulses between parts of the body.

Neurotoxicity: Poisoning of the nervous system by a neurotoxin.

Neurotoxin: A poison that acts on the nervous system.

Neurotransmitter: A chemical substance that is released at the end of a nerve fiber due to a nerve impulse, diffuses across the synaptic cleft (space between two neurons), and attached to receptors on the second nerve fiber causing the nerve impulse to be carried on.

Non-organic: A substance that does not come from living matter.

Northwest Passage: A sea route North around North America. For centuries, it was sought after as a trade route.

Organic: Relating to or coming from living matter.

Ottoman Turks: From 1299 to 1923, a Turkish empire. This was one of both the largest and longest lasting empires in history.

Oxen: A form of currency used. Oxen are worth more than both cow and sheep.

Psychoactive drug: A drug that is capable of changing a person's mood and cause perceptions to become distorted.

Pentylenetetrazol: A circulatory and respiratory stimulant used in the treatment of specific mental disorders; used to induce seizures.

Peripheral Nervous System (PNS): The parts of the nervous system other than the brain and spinal cord.

PNS: see peripheral nervous system.

Psychosis: a mental state whereby perceptions are so distorted that contact is lost with reality

Purported: Claimed or generally believed.

Receptor: An area of tissue or a molecule in a cell membrane that responds to specific neurotransmitters, hormones, or other substances.

Rheumatoid arthritis: A chronic autoimmune disease. Signs and symptoms include joint pain, swelling, stiffness, inflammation of the joints and in more severe case, the destruction/ deterioration of joints.

Safrole: Liquid obtained from the sassafras plant that is used in perfumes and soaps.

Sea Bream: A marine fish with a deeper body from back to belly than it is wide; toxins from its food accumulate in the liver and can be passed on to humans when the fish is consumed.

Sheep: A form of currency used in the 14th century. Sheep were worth less than both cow and oxen.

Serotonin: A neurotransmitter that is involved in mood, sleep, memory and other neurological functions.

Tactile: Connected with the sense of touch.

The East: The eastern portion of the Earth, mainly comprised of Asia.

Therapeutic: The treatment or curing of a disease.

The West: Includes Europe

Trimyristin: A saturated fat that is the triglyceride of myristic acid. It is found in nutmeg and makes up 20 - 25% of nutmeg.

Urinalysis: The chemical analysis of urine.

Venetians: People from Venice, Italy.

Virility: To be virile. Virile - Characteristics that are stereotypically associated as being male; masculinity, strength, energy or forcefulness.

Visigoths: A branch of Goths that invaded the Roman Empire from 3rd and 5th centuries AD.

Whooping Cough: A respiratory infection that is caused by the bacterium from the genus Bordetella (B. pertussis). Spasmodic episodes of the lungs causing a convulsive cough, that is accompanied by inhalation characterized as having a 'whooping' sound. Commonly occurs in children.

References

Abernethy, M. K.; Lance, B.; and Becker, M. D. 1992. Acute Nutmeg Intoxication. *American Journal of Emergency Medicine*, 10(5), 429-430.

Adjene, J. O.; Nwose, E. U. 2010. Histological effects of long term consumption of nutmeg on the medial geniculate body of adult Wistar rats. *North American Journal of Medical Science*; 2, 134-137. Available from: www.najms.org

Barceloux, D. G. 2008. Medical toxicology of natural substances: Foods, fungi, medicinal herbs, plants, and venomous animals. Philadelphia: John Wiley and Sons.

Beyer, J.; Ehlers, D. and Maurer, H. H. 2006. Abuse of Nutmeg (Myristica Fragrans Houtt): Studies on the Metabolism and the Toxicologic Detection of Its Ingredients Elemicin, Myristicin, and Safrole in Rat and Human Urine Using Gas Chromatography/Mass Spectrometry. *Therapeutic Drug Monitoric*, 28(4), 568-575.

Bock, M.P. 2000 . Entheology. Retrieved from: http://www.entheology.org/edoto/anmviewer.asp?a=67

Buchanan, R.L. 1978. Toxicity of spices containing methylenedioxybenzene Derivatives, a review. *Journal of Food Safety*, 1, 275-293.

Curtis, W. 2012. My nutmeg bender. The Atlantic Monthly, 309(1), 31-31. Retrieved from http://search.proquest.com/docview/917539265?accountid=11233

Demetriades, A. K.; Wallman, P. D.; McGuiness A.; Gavalas, M. C. 2005. Low cost, high risk: accidental nutmeg intoxication. *Emergency Medical Journal*, 22, 223-225

El-Alfy, A. T.; Wilson, L.; ElSohly, M. A. and Abourashed, E .A. 2009. Towards a better understanding of the psychoparmacology of nutmeg; Activities in the mouse tetrad assay. *Journal of Ethnopharmacology*, 126, 280-286.

Forrester, B. M. 2005. Nutmeg intoxication in Texas, 1998-2004. *Human and Experimental Toxicology*, 24, 563-566.

International Narcotic Control Board. January 2007. List of precursors and chemicals frequently used in the illicit manufacture of narcotic drugs and psychotropic substances under international control. Annex to Form D ("Red List"), Eleventh Edition.

Marieb, E. N. 2005. Essentials of Human Anatomy and Physiology. Benjamin Cummings.

McCann, B.; O`Gara, A. 2005. Tension viscerothorax: An important differential for tension pneumothorax. Emergency Medicine Journal, 22(10), 220-221. Retrieved from http://emj.bmj.com.subzero.lib.uoguelph.ca/content/22/3/223.full.pdf+html

McKenna, A.; Nordt, S. P. and Ryan, J. 2004. Acute nutmeg poisoning. *European Journal of Emergency Medicine:* Official Journal of the European Society for Emergency Medicine, 11(4), 240–241.

de Mello, A.C. and Carlini, E.A. 1973. Behavioral observations on compounds found in nutmeg. *Psychopharmacologia* (Berl.), 31, 349-363.

Nagano, I. 2008. Do you know about the narcotic effects of nutmeg? Humanity has used nutmeg as a medicine, narcotic, aphrodisiac, dream enhancer and inebriant. *The Entheogen Review.* Retrieved from http://www.alternet.org/drugs/140480/do_you_know_about_the_narcotic_effects_of_nutmeg

Nagano, I. 2009. Myristica fragrans: An exploration of the narcotic spice. *The Entheogen Review*, 16(1), 15-24. Retrieved from http://www.erowid.org/plants/nutmeg/nutmeg_article1.shtml

Rudgley, R. 1998. Nutmeg; The Enclyclopedia of Psychoactive Substances. Available online at www.moodfoods.com/nutmeg.index.html. Accessed May 13, 2010/

Sangalli, B. C. and Chiang, W. 2008. Toxicology of Nutmeg Abuse. *Clinical Toxicology*, 38(6), 671-678.

Shulgin, A. T. 1966. Possible implication of myristicin as a psychotropic substance. *Nature*, 310, 380-384.

Suk Lee, H.; Jeong, C.; Kim, J. 1997. In vitro and in vivo metabolism of myristicin in the rat. *Journal of Chromatography*, 367-372.

Sun Min, B.; Cuong, T. D.; Hung, T.M.; Min, B. K.; Shin, B .S.; Woo, M. H. 2011. Inhibitory effect of lignans from myristica fragnans on LPS-induced NO production in RAW264.7 cells. Bull Korean Chemical Society, 32(11). Retrieved from http://dx.doi.org/10.5012/bkcs.2011.32.11.4059

Tajuddin, S.A.; Abdul, L.; Iqbal, A.Q. and Kunwar, M.Y.A. 2005. An experimental study of sexual function improving effect of *Myristica fragrans* Houtt. (nutmeg). *BMC Complementary and Alternative Medicine*, 5(16), 1-7.

Thring, O. 2010. Consider nutmeg. Retrieved March 22, 2012, from
http://www.guardian.co.uk/lifeandstyle/wordofmouth/2010/sep/14/consider-nutmeg

Van Gils, C. and Cox, P.A. 1994. Ethnobotany of nutmeg in the Spice Islands. *Journal of Enthoparmacology*, 42, 117-124.

Wahab, A.; Ul Haq, R.;Ahmed, A.; Khan, R.; Raza, M. 2009. Anticonvulsant activities of nutmeg oil of myristica fragrans. *Phytotherapy Research*, 23, 153-158.

Wilhelmine Williams, M. 1922. The Treaty of Tordesillas and the Argentine-Brazilian Boundary Settlement. *The Hispanic American Historical Review* , Vol. 5, No. 1,pp. 3-23 Retrieved from: http://www.jstor.org/stable/2505977

Williams, S. P. 1998. The serotonin transporter: A primary target for antidepressant drugs. *Journal of Psychopharmacology*, 12(2), 115-121. Retrieved from http://jop.sagepub.com/content/12/2/115.abstract

Yuan, Z. M.; Wang, J.; Lv, J. and Jia, T. Z. 2006. Comparing analysis of components in volatile oils of nutmeg and prepared nutmeg by GC-MS. *Zhongguo Zhong Yao Za Zhi*, 31(9), 737-739.

§ 7:

Opiates - Oh so HIGH!

After missing your alarm clock, you are running late for an interview "for the job of your dreams" with a well-known pharmaceutical company. On your way out of your apartment, you manage to grab two delicious slices of lemon poppy seed cake. You scarf them down on the way there, going over your resume as well as the requirements for the job in your head. After 90 minutes, the lead interviewer calls for a break where the company asks you for a urine sample as part of a surprise drug screening process. Thinking to yourself that it's no big deal, you go to the bathroom and give them a little sample of your personal orange juice. After another gruelling two hour interview session, you head back to your apartment feeling good about your performance. A few days later, you are asked by the main interviewer to come back where he alarmingly tells you that your urine test showed the presence of morphine. Taken by complete surprise, you are only able to offer assurances that you do not use drugs of any sort. Negotiating to provide more samples for testing, you head over to the laboratory to give another little liquid sample of yourself. A few days later, you are busy with the tasks associated with your new position.

Introduction

The opium poppy (*Papaver somniferum*) may be the earliest used and misused of all medicinal plants known as mankind. Used appropriately, it could relieve severe pain effectively but misused, it could lead to the never ending suffering and distress of narcotic dependency. Indeed, the alluring opium poppy fruit pod has been a double edged sword, conferring both bliss and misery for many who have made its acquaintance. The opium poppy has made many contributions to music, the visual arts, and literature, surgery, pain relief palliative care, the growth of pharmaceutical companies and wealth, culture, wars, the illegal drug trade, addiction and human suffering. There is therefore much speculation about poppy seeds and their effect on humans.

Initial Use of Poppy Seeds

The opium poppy has been widely used, dating back hundreds of thousands of years, reaching its fateful hand into Indian, Greek and Chinese cultures and religions. Initially, it was cultivated as food as the seed is an excellent source of oil and can also be used to add a nutty taste, crunchy texture, and colour to food. It was also used in the way of religious ceremonies to find and communicate with a "higher being". It was used as a euphoriant for ritual purposes and may have been the "possession" of cultic priests. Medicinally, the Ebers Papyrus (1550 B.C.) is probably the oldest preserved medical document in existence and bears testimony to its beneficial use. It states that at the beginning, the plant was used to prevent excessive crying of children and it was also used externally as a pain-relieving agent during surgery. For a long time, it seemed to be a miracle treatment to the disease epidemics.

Opiates throughout History

Over the centuries, opium poppy cultivation spread from present day Iraq, eventually taking firm root in Egypt, Persia, India, China, and the Far East. From ancient medical writings, physicians were well aware of its great benefits as well as its dependent and addictive psychoactive effects. The writings warned physicians of the great variances in opium's strength as its contents varied considerably, depending on source and plant species. Opium was mentioned in the Greek Pharmacopoeia (5th century B.C.) and at the same time, Hippocrates wrote that poppy juice could be used both as a cathartic hypnotic narcotic and also to control bleeding.

The Greek army surgeon Dioscorides (1st century A.D.) who wrote the leading medical text of his day "De Material Media", made a distinction between the white sap from the fruit pod and a whole plant extract. He also wrote about its preparation and the disorders for which it was deemed effective. At the same time, the Roman historian Pliny the Elder wrote about the often overlooked poppy seeds which he regarded as a hypnotic while also writing that the juice was also useful for headaches, arthritis, and the curing of wounds.

Opium was introduced to India by Arab traders in the 9th century A.D. and then travelled to China 100 years later. The notable physician Avicenna wrote a famous thesis on opium and regarded it as the most powerful of all stupefacients. Using opium carefully in his medical practice, he ironically died of opium intoxication.

Between the 10th-13th centuries, opium was introduced to Europe, being hailed as a miracle cure but problems soon arose as reports of addiction soon appeared in historical writings. Soon a major opposition to anything from the Middle East including opium arose during the Holy Inquisition (1300-1500 A.D.); they were considered to be an anathema linked to the devil. This attitude continued in Europe until Paracelsus (1493-1541), who re-introduced opium to Europe during the Reformation, discovered that he could make an alcohol tincture of opium which contained all the bioactive opiates (morphine, codeine, thebaine, papeverine). Paracelsus prescribed his opium infusion for a variety of ailments including diarrhea and to alleviate pain. One must remember that disease epidemics were very common at this time and included cholera, for which opium was an effective prescription for the associated dysentery. At the time, these bioactive opiates could not be separated into their individual pure forms.

Medical Uses of Bioactive Opiates

a) Morphine

Morphine is a strong analgesic utilized to treat moderate to severe pain. While it is effective in moderating patient pain, it has several serious side effects including constipation, tolerance, dependence and withdrawal. To relieve moderate to severe pain, an adult patient must consume between 5-20 mg of morphine every 4 hours. The relieving effects will be experienced sooner if the morphine is injected, but this type of administration requires professional assistance. As noted by the National Institute of Health, the most common morphine-containing prescription drugs include: Avinza, Kadian, MS Contin, Oramorph SR, Roxanol and Roxanol-T. When abused, this substance can also lead to overdose and potentially death as it can lower respiratory rates and cause kidney failure. As a precautionary measure to help prevent addiction, prescriptions for morphine-containing drugs are not refillable. Morphine acts by mimicking endorphins which are responsible for the analgesia. Morphine predominately interacts with the mu opioid receptor binding indiscriminately within a patient's brain. Morphine acts as a receptor agonist, activating these receptors within the central nervous system. In addition, this binding is extremely strong resulting in the associated high that comes along with morphine. Morphine can also bind to kappa receptors and delta receptors.

b) Codeine

Codeine is another strong analgesic and second strongest alkaloid behind morphine. Like morphine it is used to control moderate and severe pain. Tylenol 3 is a common painkiller drug that contains 15 mg of codeine phosphate per tablet. Codeine itself is derived from methylated morphine. It has several negative side effects including nausea, vomiting, constipation, depression, tolerance and dependence. Codeine is transformed by the liver, producing norcodeine and relatives of codeine and morphine. Roughly eighty percent of codeine is converted into codeine-6-glucuronide glucuronic acid, with only five percent becoming morphine. The morphine is typically secreted by the kidney and is found to have little effect on the analgesic aspect of codeine. While it was initially believed that morphine was the active ingredient, further research has shown that codeine-6-glucuronide has the more efficient structure to bind and create the desired analgesic effect.

c) Thebaine

Thebaine is an opiate alkaloid that is chemically similar to both morphine and codeine but differs functionally. Thebaine has a stimulatory effect that, in high doses, can result in death. It can be used to create oxycodone, oxymorphone and several other pain medications. Thebaine can be considered a precursor utilized in the formation of endogenous morphine and codeine. Thebaine mimics morphine and utilizes receptors in the brain and spinal cord in a similar fashion as morphine.

d) Papaverine

While derived from the opium poppy, papaverine has large differences in structure and mechanisms compared to morphine type opium alkaloids. Typically, this opium derivative is used to treat spasms in the GI tract, bile ducts, and coronary. It can also be used as a muscle relaxant for surgery and to treat erectile dysfunction. While the exact mechanism function is unclear, it is used to inhibit the enzyme of phosphodiesterase which results in the elevation of cAMP levels. Additionally, it could potentially alter mitochondrial respiration. It also has the potential to be used as an antipsychotic. Unlike morphine and codeine, papaverine is not classified as a narcotic drug, does not possess the potential to become addictive and does not have the ability to relieve pain. As noted by the National Institute of Health, papaverine is known by the trademark Para-Time in the United States and like all other opiates, can only be prescribed by doctors.

If you think that drug addiction was a problem of the second half of the 20th century, just take a closer look at history. Without abundant scientific research and government regulation, a lot of problems were created by opiates due to its highly addictive nature. European manuscripts described opium addiction as the laudanum, with opium being a common ingredient in many over-the-counter medicines. Some bared soothing names such as "Mrs.Winslow's soothing syrup" to calm crying babies, but with 46% alcohol and 65mg morphine per ounce, no wonder the babies and infants became quiet. The British too had their own version, usually mixed with sherry of course. The English poet Samuel Coleridge wrote his infamous poem Kubla Khan during laudanum high, as he took it for medical reasons. Laudanum was recommended as a cure for all ailments including relieving women's conditions and "aches" in Victorian England and was also spoon fed to babies to quiet them. As it was a medicine, it was not subject to taxation and cost less money than a bottle of gin or sherry. In pre-probation United States, laudanum could contain 45% alcohol, 2.96 grams opium equivalent to 296 mg morphine per ounce, but varied in both alcohol and morphine content before standardization. It was no wonder that people were addicted to laudanum including Mary Todd Lincoln, wife of President Abraham Lincoln. Other notable laudanum users on both sides of the Atlantic Ocean include Lord Byron, Lewis Carroll, Samuel Coleridge, Charles Dickens, Arthur Conan Doyle, John Keats, Edgar Allan Poe, and Percy Shelley with many others knowing and writing about it also. The Wizard of Oz, one of the greatest movies ever which made Judy Garland a star in Metro Goldwyn Meyer's film crown, was probably based on an opium inspired book. In one scene, Dorothy falls deeply asleep in a poppy field before Emerald City and is eventually carried out by her friends where she recovers in the fresh air. But two things must be said in the defence of the creative artists who used laudanum is that many used it for a legitimate medical condition such as dysentery and also that each person was uniquely gifted before becoming a legal drug addict; their creativity heightened and broadened by the laudanum but they paid a heavy price, addiction to opium (morphine and codeine).

Heroin

a) "Invention" of Heroin

In the late 19th century, both Europe and North America opium based patent medicine with innocent sounding names could be bought over the counter and people became legally addicted. By this time, drug addiction began to be seen as a social problem. In the late 19th century, a British chemist invented heroin but his invention goes no further. In1898, a chemist at the now present day Bayer Pharmaceutical Company re-invented heroin as a less powerful substitute for morphine and marketed it as a cure for many ailments as well as a cure for opium (morphine) addiction. Being available in a variety of forms, it was used freely with no initial knowledge of its addictive effects. The following year, Bayer introduced acetylsalicylic acid (ASA) under the brand name Bayer Aspirin, a less harmful analgesic. Strangely enough, it required a prescription whereas heroin did not. Once the alarming addictiveness of heroin was realized a number of years later, it was removed from the general market and only became available by prescription. This was also the time when many countries started to regulate foods and drugs. The backlash to widespread drug addiction reached a crescendo with the first international drug control treaty going into force in 1919, when incorporated into the Treaty of Versailles. For better or for worse, Bayer lost some of its trademark rights to "heroin" in this treaty, following the German defeat in World War I. Up until the mid-1970s, heroin continued to be the most widely abused opiate.

b) Heroin *vs*. Morphine

The narcotic heroin is much more addictive than morphine because it is easily able to dissolve in fat and thus is able to cross the blood-brain barrier much more quickly than morphine. About two to three minutes after injection, one will experience a rush which has been described as a heightened sexual orgasm with a dramatic release of physical and psychological tension, especially in the abdomen. This rush is caused by a sudden change in the brain chemical environment as the brain quickly metabolizes heroin into morphine. This transformation essentially floods the brain with morphine causing a major imbalance in brain chemistry which completely disrupts normal bodily functioning. It not only blocks any perception of pain but also produces the characteristic euphoric high as the drug binds to a variety of opioid receptors in the reward circuitry of the brain. This high feeling can last from four to five hours as the tissues in the rest of the body are also able to metabolize the heroin into morphine. Morphine is not as addictive as some other drugs such as heroin because it does not cross the blood-brain barrier as quickly. Morphine will first cause a "cozy" state wherein the person is oblivious to the world around them. As the drug begins to take effect in the brain, the user will experience flu-like systems for the next 8-12 hours including nausea, muscle spasm and cramps, anxiety, fever, diarrhea and goose bumps. The symptoms will increase in intensity over 2-3 days, and then eventually disappear in 7-10 days once the brain has re-established its normal brain chemistry.

Opium addiction was not just a problem in Europe and North America as it had long been such in The Middle East and eastwards to Japan. The British East India Company paid for

Chinese tea with silver but as they could not get their hands on enough of it to balance the trade deficit, they turned to opium from India where they had procured exclusive rights to it. As it does not take a rocket scientist to figure it out, China fell under the opium spell. Despite prohibition and attempted banning of trade, opium addiction continued to escalate these actions and forced the trade underground. In the 19th century, China once again tried to ban opium importation but the British sought to protect their vested "interests" and, upon reflection, they were essentially no different than the current drug dealers. Both countries fought two wars over this issue (1839-1842, 1856-1860) with China losing the Opium Wars, the original war on drugs. Under treaty, China had to pay reparation to British merchants as well as surrendering Hong Kong Island to the British with the British holding on tight until 1997, a long 155 years. Unfortunately, Chinese people who came to North America to build the railway were, to a degree, regarded as drug addicts and sadly were treated much worse.

The Alkaloid Content of Opium

In its natural state, opium varies in composition based on how, where and when it is extracted from the opium poppy. The opaque milky sap found inside the opium fruit pod consists of 5-20% water, 20 % sugar and 10-20 % alkaloids. In total, the opium poppy is the source for more than 30 different alkaloids. There are, however, 5 main alkaloids that make up the bulk of this 10-20%; morphine (8-17%), codeine (7%), thebaine (0.1-2.5%), papaverine (0.5-1.5%) and noscapine (1-10%). Alkaloids are naturally occurring, nitrogen-rich compounds, which can easily be recognized by the "ine" suffix at the end of their names. Despite the fact that they are very bitter tasting and can be extremely poisonous, natural and semi-synthetic alkaloids are commonly found in a variety of foods, medicines, and pesticides. For example, tobacco contains nicotine, coffee contains caffeine, and cocoa leaves contain cocaine. All alkaloids have various degrees of psychoactive characteristics such as tolerance, dependency and addiction and elicit effects including euphoria, hallucinations, stimulation, or depression. The alkaloids found within the black opium poppy are called opioids as they cause both psychoactive characteristics in the central nervous system (CNS) and physical effects in the gastrointestinal (GI) tract. The black opium poppy is the source of both the natural opioids (morphine, codeine, and thebaine) and the semi-synthetic opioids which are produced from the natural sources (heroin, hydromorphone, hydrocodone, oxycodone, *etc.*). About 90% of the world's morphine is extracted from opium straw, the dried mature opium plant minus the mature seeds, as well as from the leaves. Opioids are also obtained from the maturing opium fruit pod by scoring it with a small sharp knife to allow the "bleeding" wound to ooze a white sticky sap, a process which is repeated many times until mature. Scored in the evening, the chemicals in the white sap are exposed to the air during cooler night temperatures, resulting in the production of a solid brown mass by daylight. Through a relatively simple laboratory process, the morphine extracted from the opium can easily be chemically altered into its highly potent cousin, heroin.

Opium Consumption within the Diet

a) Poppy Seeds

Opium is a regulated substance; however the general public has easy access to it in small doses via opium poppy seeds. Poppy seeds are tiny bluish-greyish black seeds with low morphine content. What many people may not know is that poppy seeds are derived from the opium poppy flower, the same plant that produces morphine and codeine. These seeds are of more value to bakers and food connoisseurs than to drug dealers as they add a distinctive nutty flavour and crunchy texture to foods. Harvested when mature, the opium fruit pod is split open to reveal a large number of hidden seeds. Even though the bulk of the psychoactive ingredients are found in other plant tissues, some of the alkaloids remain on the outside of the seeds, even after washing and processing. The morphine content of a poppy seed ranges from 4-20 mg per kilogram, with an average of 12 mg per kilogram.

To relieve moderate to severe pain in an adult, a dose of morphine of 5-20 mg every four to five hours is required. With this information, it is possible to calculate the amount of poppy seeds that one would need to eat in order to achieve a high. Taking the lower value of 5 mg as a dose, one would need to ingest 0.5 kg of poppy seeds to experience any kind of high. It is estimated that an average poppy seed bagel contains approximately 820 mg of poppy seeds - this is just less than one gram. Doing the math, one would have to eat slightly more than 500 bagels in order to ingest the minimum amount of morphine required to feel an effect.

Another look at how much poppy seeds it would take to feel an effect is a study comparing white and blue poppy seeds. They were analyzed to see if they contained morphine and codeine using chromatography. The poppy seeds were crushed and treated with chemicals and then made alkaline and then treated again. Then the alkaloid factors were extracted and measured using gas chromatography. The white poppy seed had 0.6 to 4.2 ppm of morphine and 0.5 to 1.5 ppm of codeine and the blue poppy seed had 0.5 to 1.7 ppm of free morphine and 0.1 to 0.5 ppm of codeine. Although these "drugs" are present in the poppy seeds, the study states that one would have to ingest 3.5 kg of poppy seeds for them to experience a "high".

b) Poppy Seed Tea

Drinking poppy seed tea is another option for getting high. This special tea cannot be made by simply stirring poppy seeds in hot water because morphine does not dissolve in water. Instead, the morphine can be extracted from the poppy seeds by soaking them in warm lemon juice solution. The morphine combines with the citric acid within the lemon juice to form a morphine-citrate complex which is able to dissolve in water. Its popularity is likely due to the fact that poppy seeds are inexpensive and easy to obtain, as they are a common baking ingredient. It would still take 0.5kg of poppy seeds, however, to successfully get a high from drinking this foul tasting tea.

Although it sounds innocent enough, poppy seed tea can actually be extremely dangerous. There have been many cases of death due to poppy seed tea and in most of the cases, the deceased are young adults who were looking for a cheap, fast high. The cause of death is overdose. Since the effects of opiates include sedation and depressed breathing, an overdose would cause a victim to become oxygen deprived and go into cardiac arrest. A California teen took this route to get high and ended up dead after ingesting four times the lethal dose of morphine and codeine. The overdoses caused by poppy seed tea are most likely accidental. In poppy seeds sold at the grocery store, there are varying amounts of morphine and other opiates that would be dissolved into the tea when it is made. This means that each time the tea is made, it may have a different level of potency and the consumer would not have any way of knowing. Repeated consumption of poppy seed tea can lead to morphine tolerance, dependence and finally addiction.

c) Studies on Poppy Seeds in the Diet

Poppy seeds have several places of origins including Australia, Hungary, and Turkey. Poppy seeds from these locations and others were tested and they all had a wide variation of morphine and codeine but did not contain any other opiates. Volunteers also ingested the amount of poppy seeds from the same origin on two bagels. The results came out positive up to twenty four hours after ingestion where the results then became negative. This study proves that consuming a poppy seed bagel before a random drug screening (like in the example at the beginning of the chapter) can affect the outcome of the test.

There have been many studies done in which participants will consume poppy seeds then give a urine sample to see if the researchers can detect any morphine or codeine in the urine. Selavka (1991) stated in her research that the poppy seed bagels, cakes, and muffins that participants consumed did not contain enough poppy seeds to give rise to opiate positive specimens results. A number of the participants, however, had positive according to the National institute of Drug Abuse cut off level. As the example in the chapter, eating a product that contains poppy seeds could affect the amount of morphine or codeine found in your urine. It must also be kept in mind that some poppy seeds containing high levels of these alkaloids could be available or being used in products consumers are buying. Perz et al. (2007) tested different poppy seeds used on bagels and sold to consumers. They discovered that all poppy seeds varied in the amount of morphine they contained. These results are highly possible because recommendations for alkaloid reducing measurement are often not followed (Perz et al. 2007).

d) Cooking with Poppy Seeds

In the article "Opiates in Poppy Seed: Effect on Urinalysis Results after Consumption of Poppy Seed Cake-Filling", it is discussed how the consumption of a cake with poppy seed filling will produce urine with morphine in it. The study says that poppy seeds are seen in everyday cooking in Europe. It said that morphine concentrations in poppy seed purchased in Sweden ranged from 2.6 to 106.7 µg/L which is a substantial amount of morphine! The purpose of this article was to see how much morphine was present in poppy seed fillings that were imported to the U.S (please note that poppies are not grown in the U.S). To analyze, the filling was heated with chemicals and then cooled and the morphine product was extracted and measured. The other way to analyze the amount of morphine that a human was ingesting was that certain individuals ingested these poppy seed filling and their urine sample was tested in every five hours to see how much morphine was present. The chart below shows the results of subject four.

e) Limiting the Consumption of Poppy Seeds

Recently, the consumption of poppy seeds has raised concern as there have been cases of reported intoxication. The Federal Institute for Risk Assessment (FIRA) has issued a limit to the amount of poppy seeds present in food to 4 mg/kg. Limits of 10 mg/kg have been deemed unsafe to consume as it can cause intoxicating effects. The FIRA, however, disregarded the influence of food preparation and processes that can affect the effectiveness of morphine. When poppy seeds are used as a topping such as on bagels, the amount of poppy seeds can exceed 100 mg/kg and when consumed, will not even exceed the tolerable intake level of morphine at 0.38 mg. Even with these limitations, with the knowledge of morphine alkaloids found on poppy seeds, it has been found to have many abusers of the substance. In New Zealand, many opium abusers are taking large quantities of dried poppy seeds and soaking them in water to release the alkaloids found on the seed coat. The water containing any of the residuals from the seeds is then ingested.

Legal View on Opiates

Although opium for commercial pharmaceutical use is grown with special government license around the world, there is some confusion in the law. The U.S law enforcement is somewhat inconsistent about this plant. If poppies are grown as a source for opiate, it violates the CSA (Control Substance Act). But if they are grown for ornamental purposes, their legal position is somewhat less clear, since they are widely grown and available.

Canadian schedules are very different than US, where opium is schedule II. Here in Canada, opium poppy, a controlled substance, is under schedule I in the psychotropic substance control list of CDSA (Canada Controlled Drug and Substance Act). The stereoisomers of substances in schedule I are also controlled. CDSA has detailed eight schedules of substances that are controlled. The schedules are used to simplify the various punitive sentences associated with different classification of material for different offenses. In case of possession, schedule I substances carry a maximum of seven years imprisonment whereas schedule III substances carry a maximum of three years. The current law prohibits possession, trafficking, production and exportation of opium poppy derivatives such as PCP, methamphetamine, codeine when not in a medicine, with at least two other active ingredients.

Australia, Turkey and India are major producers of poppy for medicinal purposes, and poppy-based drugs. The U.S has a policy of sourcing 80% of its narcotic raw material from traditional producers; India and Turkey, but partially on the basis of the assertion that there is an acute global shortage of opium poppy based medicines, some of which are on the WHO list of essential drugs. The Senile Council (the international council on security and development) proposes licensing poppy products in Afghanistan and today, it is the world's largest producer of opiate, accounting ninety three percent of global opium. Nowadays, opiates containing medicines belong to the Narcotic Drugs category that can be only available to the public through doctor prescription. In a United Nation International Narcotic Control Board Report, the medical properties of opiates stated that it can be used as an anaesthetic or analgesic, to treat diarrhea, cough or narcotic addiction, as well as for veterinary and dental purposes. Even with the benefits clearly stated, the danger of the plant is unavoidable. So the board will cooperate with governments and World Health Organization to meet the demand of opiates for medical and scientific usage as well as preventing drug abuse.

While the results of the initial drug test for the job were surprising, they were not totally unexpected as two pieces of cake loaded with poppy seeds can cause a positive result in a urine screening test. Fortunately, this has been recognized and the detection level in these tests has been increased to prevent the positive results based on the poppy seed defence. While opioid drugs have made a great contribution to the health and well-being of mankind, it can also extend its hook and draw one into its sticky web of addiction, dependency and withdrawal.

Glossary

Acetylsalicylic Acid (ASA): Also known as aspirin, ASA is used to treat a number of different problems such as headache, fever and general mild pain in adults.

Addiction: Chronic consumption of a substance that involves a compulsive need to obtain the substance, tolerance, dependence, and detrimental effects on the person's health and overall life.

Alcohol Tincture: Used to make herbal extracts from plants as the alcohol dissolves the majority of constituents in most herbs.

Alkaloid: Naturally occurring nitrogen-rich chemical compound.

Analgesia: State of painlessness without unconsciousness.

Analgesic: A remedy that relieves pain.

Anathema: A person who is attested or loathed, associated with damnation or destruction.

Antipsychotic: A substance used in the treatment of psychosis, paranoia, or depression.

Autonomic Nervous System: The autonomic nervous system regulates key functions of the body including the activity of the heart muscle, the smooth muscles (*e.g.*, the muscles of the intestinal tract), and the glands.

Bile duct: The tube that carries bile from the gallbladder and liver into the upper part of the small intestine; bile is a yellow or greenish liquid that aids in the absorption and digestion of fats.

Bioactive: Causing an effect or reaction in living tissue.

Bloating: To swell up or inflate with liquid or gas.

Blood-brain barrier: A layer of tightly packed cells which prevents most compounds in the blood from freely flowing into the brain.

Bronchitis: A painful and irritating swelling of the bronchi branches in the lungs.

cAMP (cyclic adenosine monophosphate): An important secondary messenger molecule in the body involved in the transmission of signals within cells.

Cathartic Hypnotic Narcotic: A drug or other substance sold for nonmedical purposes, which affects mood or behaviour, provides psychological relief through the expression of strong emotions, and induces sleep.

Cholera: An infectious disease caused by the bacterium *Vibrio* cholera which releases a poisonous toxin that causes increased release of water in the intestines and thus produces severe diarrhea.

Central Nervous System (CNS): The brain and spinal cord in the human body make up the central nervous system.

Chromatography: The separation of mixtures into their constituents.

Constipation: A state where it is hard to make a bowel movement because the feces are hard and dry.

Controlled Substance Act: Under United States law, the Controlled Substance Act is the policy that regulates the manufacturing, possession, and distribution of controlled substances.

Coronary: Referring to the heart muscle.

Crescendo: A slow and steady increase in volume or force.

Dependence: Reliance on a substance for normal functioning that produces withdrawal symptoms if the substance is taken awa.y

Dopamine: A feel-good neurotransmitter and hormone produced by the brain.

Dysentery: A disease caused by inflammation of the lower bowels that leads to mucous diarrhea.

Endogenous: Starting from within, internally.

Endorphins: Natural painkiller molecules produced by the pituitary gland within the brain that have an analgesic effect similar to that of opioids.

Epidemic: A temporary increase in the incidence rate of a disease; the disease is widespread and affects many people at one time.

Erectile Dysfunction: A condition in which a male has difficulty achieving and maintaining an erection.

Euphoria: Intense state of happiness and well-being.

Fruit pod: A structure of a plant that contains its seeds.

GABA (gamma-aminobutyric acid): An inhibitory neurotransmitter in the body; GABA transfers a signal from a nerve cell to a target cell, which decreases the probability that the target cell will fire off its own signal - the signal-sending ability of the target cell is thus inhibited.

Gastrointestinal (GI) Tract: The stomach and intestine working together as a functional unit.

Glomerulonephritis: A disease of the kidney that affects tiny vessels known as capillaries.

Heroin: A semi-synthetic opioid made from morphine that is commonly abused when used as a drug.

Hippocrates: A Greek doctor, "Father of Medicine".

Hypnotic: An agent or drug that produces hypnosis, sleep or sedation.

Inflammation: A localized physical condition in which part of the body becomes reddened, swollen, hot, and often painful, especially as a reaction to injury or infection.

Intoxication: the act of drunkenness.

Intravenous: Existing, taking place within, or administered into a vein or veins.

Metabolize: To subject a substance to be broken down to yield energy necessary for survival.
Methylated: An organic compound in which the hydrogen of the hydroxyl group (OH) of a methyl alcohol (CH_3OH) is replaced by a metal (CH_3O-metal) .

Morphine: The most abundant alkaloid found in opium poppy which possesses pain relieving abilities.

Narcotic: Any substance that dulls the senses.

Neurotransmitters: Chemical that transmits information across a junction (synapse) that separates one nerve cell (neuron) from another nerve cell or a muscle; the actions of some drugs mimic those of naturally occurring neurotransmitters.

Norcodeine: An opiate compound with a molecular structure closely related to codeine; norcodeine has relatively little opioid activity on its own but is formed as a by-product of codeine metabolism following ingestion.

Nucleus Accumbens: A collection of neurons in the brain that is said to have an important role in pleasure, addiction, aggression, fear, and the placebo effect.

Opioid: Chemical that binds to specific receptors in the body, primarily in the nervous system and gastrointestinal tract, which produces characteristic effects, including analgesia and euphoria.

Opium Infusion: An injection of opium administered into a vein or beneath the skin to provide control of pain in a dying patient.

Opium Straw: Also known as "poppy straw", a term used to describe the dried stems/upper stalks and pod of the plant; stems or "straws" of the poppy were used to extract the chemical before it was known that a greater amount of chemical was found in the capsules of the plant.

Oxycodone: A narcotic alkaloid related to codeine, used as an analgesic and a sedative chiefly in the form of its hydrochloride salt.

Oxymorphone: A potent morphine-derived narcotic analgesic, used as a substitute for morphine

Peristalsis: A series of organized muscle contractions that occur throughout the digestive tract; it is an automatic and important process that moves food through the digestive system; it also moves urine from the kidneys into the bladder, and bile from the gallbladder into the intestine.

Phosphodiesterase: An enzyme (protein within the body that speeds up the rate of chemical reactions) that breaks apart the backbone connections of DNA (phosphodiester bonds); inhibitors of this enzyme will prolong or enhance certain physiological processes.

Pituitary Gland: A small gland located within the hypothalamus of the brain that functions to control all other glands of the endocrine system, ensuring proper release of hormones.

Pneumonia: Respiratory condition in which there is an infection of the lungs.

Potency: The capacity of something to be very strong.

Psychoactive: Substance that alters brain function in terms of consciousness, behaviour, mood, perception, or cognition.

Renal: Referring to the kidneys; renal physiology is the study of kidney function.

Reward Circuitry: The release of dopamine (a feel good neurotransmitter) within the brain as a result of an action such as exercise; drugs are able to activate this system, which can lead to addiction.

Schedule I Drugs: Drugs which have a high risk of abuse and are not considered legal for medical use.

Secondary Chemicals: Chemicals which act as telegram messengers to deliver a signal between the cell which produces the chemical and a target cell.

Sedation: Sedation is the depression of a patient's awareness to the environment and reduction of his or her responsiveness to external stimulation.

Sedative: A substance that leads to calming or soothing feelings.

Semi-synthetic: Derived synthetically from one or more substances of natural origin.

Stereoisomer: Any of a group of isomers in which atoms are linked in the same order but differ in their spatial arrangement.

Stupefacients: A drug or substance that causes a sluggish daze comparable to sleepiness or drowsiness.

Tolerance: Decrease in the response to a stimulus (*e.g.* opioid) after prolonged exposure or chronic use.

Ulcers: A painful open sore that can develop in the stomach or small intestine; ulcers are commonly caused by *Helicobacter pylori* bacteria.

References

Ballabh, P.; Braun, A.; Nedergaard, M. 2004. The blood-brain barrier: an overview: structure, regulation, and clinical implications. U.S. National Library of Medicine National Institutes of Health. 16(1):1-13. http://www.ncbi.nlm.nih.gov/pubmed/15207256

Brandt, M.; Fischer, R. J.; Buchen, K.; Hamprecht, C.; Moroder, B.; Wunsch, E. 1976 Enkephalin regulates the levels of cyclic nucleotides in neuroblastoma X glioma hybrid cells. *Nature,* 262, 311–313.

Braye, K.; Harwood, T.; Inder, R.; Beasley, R.; Robinson, G. 2007. Poppy seed tea and opiate abuse in New Zealand. *Drug and Alcohol Review*, 26, 215-219.

Breivik, E. K.; Barkvoll, P.; and Skovlund, E. 1999. Combining diclofenac with acetaminophen or acetaminophen-codeine after oral surgery: A randomized, double-blind single-dose study. *Clinical Pharmacology and Therapeutics*, 66, 625-635.

Brownstein, M. 1993. A brief history of opiates, opioid peptides, and opioid receptor. *Proceedings of the National Academy of Sciences of the United States of America* , 70, 5391-5393.

Brundege, J. M.; Williams, J. T. 2002. Differential Modulation of Nucleus Accumbens Synapses. *Journal of Neuropsychology,* 88(1), 142-151.

Chien, C. C.; Pasternak, G. W. 1995. Sigma antagonists potentiate opioid analgesia in rats. *Neuroscience* 190(2): 137-139.

Cloe, A. 2009. Opiate withdrawal symptoms. Retrieved from http://www.livestrong.com/article/60656-opiate-withdrawal-symptoms

Clouse, R. 2010. Opiate addiction symptoms. Retrieved from http://www.livestrong.com/article/184007-opiate-addiction-symptoms/

Conti M. 2000. Phosphodiesterases and Cyclic Nucleotide Signalling in Endocrine Cells. *Molecular Endocrinology* 14(9): 1317-1327.

Controlled Drug and Substances Act, retrieved from www.CDSA.ca

Corbett, A.; McKnight, S.; Henderson, G.; Opioid Receptors [Internet]. Available from: http://opioids.com/receptors/

Crain, S.; Shen, K. 1996. Modulatory effects of Gs-coupled excitatory opioid receptor functions on opioid analgesia, tolerance, and dependence *Neurochemical Research*. 21(11), 1347-1351.

Crowe, A. V.; Howse, M.; Bell, G. M.; Henr, J. A. 2000. Substance Abuse and the Kidney. *QJM*, 93. 147-152.

Daglish, M. R C.; Williams, T. M.; Wilson, Sue J.; Taylor, L. G.; Eap, C. B.; Augsburger, M.; Giroud, C.; Brooks, D. J.; Myles, J .S.; Grasby, P.; Lingford-Hughes, A. R.; and Nutt, D. J. 2008. Brain dopamine response in human opioid addiction. *The British Journal of Psychiatry*, 193, 65-72.

Gasche, Y.; Daali, Y.; Fathi, M.; Chiappe, A., Cottini, S.; Dayer, P.; and Desmeules, P. J. 2004. Codeine Intoxication Associated with Ultrarapid CYP2D6 Metabolism. *The New England Journal of Medicine*, 351(27), 2827-2831.

Grove, M. D.; Spencer, G. F.; Wakeman, M. V.; Tookey, H L. 1967. Morphine and Codeine in Poppy Seeds. *Journal of Agricultural and Food Chemistry*. 24: 896-897.

Harrelson T. 2011. Three Main Reasons for Using Alcohol in Tinctures [Internet]. [cited 2011 July 24]. Available from: http://healingtools.tripod.com/alctinc.html

Holder, A. 2010. Drugs, diseases and procedures. Sedation. Retrieved from: http://emedicine.medscape.com/article/809993-overview

Holzer, P. 2009. Regulatory Peptides. *Opiod Receptors in the Gastrointestinal Tract*, 155. (1-3), 11-17.

Howell, E. 2004. Medscape Psychiatry. Addiction and reward circuitry in the brain. Retrieved from: http://www.medscape.com/viewarticle/472497

Hurley, R. A.; Hayman, L.A.; Taber, K. H. 2007. Is Opiate Addiction Associated With Longstanding Neurobiological Changes? *The Journal of Neuropsychiatry and Clinical Neurosciences*, 19(3), 242-248.

Jewell, S. 2011. Long term effects of opiate use. Retrieved from http://www.livestrong.com/article/72769-longterm-effects-opiate-use/

Kaushal, M. 2011. Opiate withdrawal side effects. Retrieved from http://www.livestrong.com/article/120322-opiate-withdrawal-side-effects/

The Kidney Foundation of Canada. 2002. What is kidney disease? Retrieved from: http://www.kidney.ca/Page.aspx?pid=320

Laurie, S. 2008. Codeine use while breastfeeding may be dangerous [Internet]. Canada: CTV NEWS – Bell Media; [cited 2011 July 21]. Available from: http://www.ctv.ca/CTVNews/Canada/20080820/tylenol_3_breastfeeding_080820/

Mikus, G.; Somogyi, A.A.; Bochner, F.; Eichelbaum, M. 1991. Thebaine O-demethylation to oripavine: genetic differences between two rat strains. *Xenobiotica*. 21(11):1501-1509.

Møller, M. R.; Hammer, K., and Engel, O. 2004. Poppy seed consumption and toxicological analysis of blood and urine samples. *Forensic Science International*, 142(2), 183-186.

Perk, G. Hanna, S.; and Stalnikowicz, R. 2003. Lethal oral papaverine overdose. *The American Journal of Emergency Medicine*, 21(3), 245.

Perz, R. C.; Sproll, C.; Lachenmeier, D.W.; and Bushchmann, R. 2007. Opiate alkaloids in poppy seeds - a consequence of globalisation of trade? *Deutsche Lebensmittel-Rundschau, German Food Review*, 103, 193-196.

Pelders, M.; Ros, J. 1996. "Poppy seeds: differences in morphine and codeine content and variation in inter- and intra-individual excretion." *Journal of Forensic Science*. 41(2): 209-212.

Pettitt, B .C.; Dyszel, S. M.; Hood, L. V. 1967. Opiates in Poppy Seed: Effect on Urinalysis Results after Consumption of Poppy Seed Cake-Filling. *Clinical Chemistry*. 33, 1251-1252.

Portenoy, R.,Thaler, H., Inturrisi, C.,Friedlander-Klar, H., Foley, K. 1992. The metabolite morphine-6-glucuronide contributes to the analgesia produced by morphine infusion in patients with pain and normal renal function. *Clinical Pharmacology and Therapeutics*. 51, 422-443.

Pub Med Health. 2010. Pneumonia. Bronchopneumonia; Community-acquired pneumonia. Retrieved from: http://www.ncbi.nlm.nih.gov/pubmedhealth/PMH0001200/

Roy, S. D.; and Flynn, G. L. 1998. Solubility Behavior of Narcotic Analgesics in Aqueous Media: Solubilities and Dissociation Constants of Morphine, Fentanyl, and Sufentanil. *Pharmaceutical Research*, 6(2), 147-151.

Tomkins, D. M.; and Sellers, E. M. 2001. Addiction and the brain: the role of neurotransmitters in the cause and treatment of drug dependence -a review. *Journal of the Canadian Medical Association*, 164(6), 817-821.

Waldhoer, M.; Bartlett, S. E.; and Whistler, J. L. 2004. Opioid Rerceptors. *Annual Review of Biochemistry*, 73, 953-990.

Williams, T. M.; Daglish, M. R. C.; Lingford-Hughes, A.; Taylor, L.G.; Hammers, A.; Brooks, D .J.; Grasby, P.; Myles, J. S.; and Nutt, D. J. 2007. Brain opioid receptor binding in early abstinence from opioid dependence: Positron emission tomography study. *The British Journal of Psychiatry*, 191, 63-69.

Ye, K.; Ke, Y.; Keshava, N.; Shanks, J.; Kapp, J.; Tekmal, R.; Petros, J.; and Joshi, H. 1998. Opium alkaloid noscapine is an antitumor agent that arrests metaphase and induces apoptosis in dividing cells. *Proceedings of the National Academy of Sciences of the United States of America*, 95(4), 1601-1606.

§ 8:

Wanna get HIGH?

Reach for Rye!

Having recently graduated from university, you begin your research career working in a government research laboratory. Most of the work is routine, but one day your supervisor calls you to her office, and looking nervously around, she closes the door. Before you can say one word, she asks if you can keep your lips sealed, and giving her your assurances, she points to the box on her desk. "It seems", she says, "that there has been an outbreak of a fungal disease in some of our country's most economically important cereal grains which can affect both national and international trade." As she continues, the tenseness in the office becomes thicker and her voice has a higher pitch. "The government has requested that this stays within these four walls as any leak would cause panic ... some of these grains have already been made into foods for the retail market. If any information leaks out prematurely, it would cause panic. Analyze the samples and get back to me with a detailed report. I will expect it on my desk within three days." Walking out stunned like a deer in headlights, you shake your head wondering what just happened. Am I going to keep government secrets now? Is this part of my job description? Following protocol, you start your initial analysis in a biohazard chamber with your lab book and then proceed to open the box. Inside you find grain and flour samples from rye, barley, wheat, and oats in individual hermetically sealed bags. Having focused on cereal toxins during graduate studies in Food Science, you inspect the seeds closely and find some suspicious evidence which look like a plant disease called Ergot, but do not see any specks in the flours. Taking this as an encouraging sign, you then examine the samples under the microscope, and record all your observations in the lab book. Securing the samples, you then head off to the university library to investigate current techniques in ergot analysis and also to gain more up-to-date information about ergot itself. Quickly finding the information you need and also securing the expertise of former professors, you settle in for three long days of very intensive secretive work. You kiss the long three day holiday weekend at the cottage goodbye! Microorganisms are invisible to the naked eye and include a large group of very small plants (like plankton), animals, bacteria, and certain fungi. The latter group (fungi) is divided into yeasts, moulds, and mushrooms, the latter including the most infamous, elusive, and expensive white and black truffles and the well camouflaged Morels. These non-photosynthetic organisms can only be detected by sight when they are fruiting or by odour to specially trained dogs or pigs. Many fungi are deceptively innocent-looking while camouflaging the presence of powerful toxic chemicals called mycotoxins that may cause effects such as hallucinations, illness and death. These ever-present strange organisms not only colonize decaying matter but also foods such as cereals, nuts, fruit, coffee, cocoa, spices, nuts, and milk in order to survive. All in all, they cause havoc for farmers and producers alike by spoiling a whopping 10,000,000,000 (10^9) tons of food every year, about 25% of total global food production. With numbers like these, the economic impact for small scale farmers is huge and may even threaten their very existence.

With the seeming endless power of modern pharmaceutical drugs, one gets lulled into thinking that synthetic man-made drugs are more dangerous than natural ones, as mankind likes to "tinker" with the natural versions. But indeed the most dangerous compounds are natural with aflatoxin (peanuts), botulinum (honey and improperly fermented fish), and tetradotoxin (puffer fish) being the three most deadly. The fungi especially are very creative and extremely inventive producing more than 300 different toxic substances called mycotoxins, each one having very different chemical structures, drug-like effects, dosage requirements and duration, effective time of action, and target tissue or organ. Most mycotoxins do not cause death instantly but can cause many diseases including cancer and the suppression of the immune system; not so much from one single dose but by the consistent regular exposure to subclinical amounts.

Different fungal species belonging to the Genus *Claviceps* have been, and continue to be, a curse to the human population as they parasitize the reproductive organs of the cereal grain and forage grasses as soon as their flowers open. The result produces a purple curved fruiting structure called a sclerotium which contains the toxic mycotoxins. Its colour and shape resemble a cock's spur, hence the name Ergot; the descriptive word and a gift from the French. When separated from the healthy seeds, these grains look more like dried rat poop. The word "ergot" was not coined until 1683 when it described "that malignity breeding in the ears of corn which contain certain black grains called, in Sologne (a region in France), Ergots and in Gastinoise, Bled Cornue". Humans and other mammals consuming infected food, or even just inhaling grain dust infected with a fungal toxin, can develop a disease called mycotoxicosis. In the case of Ergot, it is called ergotism which has two forms, with the fungus Claviceps purpurea being the culprit. Fortunately, however, only one form rears its ugly head at a time, but simultaneous outbreaks have occurred, albeit rarely, once in France (1085) while Russia has unfortunately experienced many outbreaks during the 18th and 19th centuries.

The earliest descriptions of ergot and its effects are from the Middle East, the "birthplace" of many wild grasses (grains) which we use in valuable sources of food. The first account is on an Assyrian cuneiform tablet (600 B.C.) which notes a "noxious pustule in the ear of grain" and a sacred Parsee book (400-300 B.C.) makes the observation that these grasses cause pregnant women to drop the womb and die in childbirth. The exact identity is not known but the Assyrian record indicates that it was at least an unwelcome contaminant; most likely in a cereal crop with some importance. If not so, why would the person go to the effort and expense of chiselling it into a stone tablet? Most likely the grain was either wheat or (wild?) rye, with wheat being the most likely candidate as it was an important staple in the Middle Eastern diet at the time. While rye is also endemic to the same area, it was most likely collected from the wild rather than cultivated, and it has never been a staple in either Greek or Roman cuisine. The Roman historian Pliny the Elder knew of rye, but dismissed it outright as he considered it to be very poor food which barely averted starvation. Even mixing it with spelt grain did not mask its unpalatable bitter taste! Pliny complained that it did not digest well in the stomach. Based on this information, it sounds that his experience of rye was from firsthand knowledge as he traveled with the Roman legions in either France or Germany.

The introduction of rye into Europe during the early Christian era seems to have opened a Pandora's Box which spewed its detestable contents far and wide as ergot outbreaks became common in many countries. Just like the Bubonic Plague (1300s-1400s) and the Irish potato famine (1845-1852), ergotism affected human destiny by causing much morbidity and mortality in Europe, Russia, and some parts of North America. The ergot infected grain was unknowingly ground into flour and then baked into bread. Being the same colour as the flour, the dark coloured sclerotia were difficult to see, although it could be seen as dark specks in pasta. Likewise, the presence of ergot could not be detected by taste either as the insidious toxic chemicals was masked by additives such as salt or sugar. This may have many functions in bread including the masking of the bitter rye flavour or alternatively could have been achieved by the spoiled (oxidized) flour. It is claimed that the Roman legion in Gaul (France) experienced at least one outbreak of ergotism, but this cannot be substantiated from the historical writings. The earliest known European case of ergot poisoning was of the gangrene type which burst onto the scene in 9th century France when thousands of people died, the reports bemoaning that "a great plague of swollen blisters consumed the people by a loathsome rot, so that their limbs loosened and fell off before death. " Between the 10th-12th centuries, it is estimated that 50,000 people died of ergotism in France alone. This at the time was huge and is still so, even by today's standards. It decimated the population again and again, and caused extreme fear and anxiety. In the Middle Ages, the excruciating burning sensation in the limbs became known as "ignis sacer" or "holy fire", and these symptoms were believed to be a sign of divine wrath and judgment. So serious were these outbreaks that The Catholic Church invoked the help of St. Anthony, a 3rd century reclusive hermit who had lived in the Egyptian desert. The burning associated with ergotism received the nickname "St. Anthony's Fire" as its patron saint had suffered much in the hot scorching desert. Thousands of people made laborious pilgrimages to his shrine and many received miraculous healings during their long journeys. While this may have been from consuming non-contaminated bread, it still is a miracle as these healings only occurred when the Church invoked the help of a saint from a distant land.

The ergot chemicals not only cause gangrenous ergotism but also a convulsive form. Between calm periods characterized by a ravenous appetite, the unfortunate victim of convulsive ergotism suffers epileptic seizures, spastic movements of the limbs, dance-like twitching, a burning which felt like thousands of stinging ants, and sweating. The first definitive European outbreak occurred in 1556 in Germany and its characteristic symptoms were associated with "St. Virus's Dance". Across the Atlantic Ocean in the United States, convulsive ergotism was a part of the Great Awakening in the New England area (mid-18th century) with old world superstitions abounding. Convulsive ergotism was believed to be a sign of bewitchment with its sufferers deemed to be possessed by demons, and they were unfortunately also treated as such. Likewise, people of Finmark (Norway) experienced the same thing with many people, mostly women, accused of witchcraft and condemned to death. In 18th Europe, however, the opinion started to change at the dawning of the Age of Enlightenment. Reason interpreted the convulsions to be signs of Divine favour, a holy possession marked by visions, hallucinations, trances, ecstatic spasms, unimaginable contortions, and profuse sweating.

In Europe, rye and wheat were used to make staple foods such as bread, as well as beer, which were considered to be a safe source of fluid as the safety of drinking water could not be guaranteed until the 18th-19th centuries. For a long time, it was suspected that ergotism was related to diet, but it was not until 1676 that ergot contamination in rye was definitively established as the cause of gangrenous ergotism, with the convulsive form identified in 1695. In response to the 1676 discovery, grain beating and sieving were introduced in France which essentially stopped the outbreaks, although ergotism continued to plague the rest of Europe. Recent studies of ergot chemicals in foods produced from traditional ergot grains have indicated that their persistence, concentration, and stability are quite constant. Even with control measures, food and beverages from many European countries have ergot alkaloids present in amounts greater than 1000 μg/kg. The total amount, however, is affected by bread-making and can reduce concentrations by as much as 50%. This reduction also occurs in beer-making with some chemicals still present in the final product. The reduction in bread-making, however, is not well-balanced due to the increased concentrations of some ergot chemical while other chemical become more active. While encouraging for today, the results would not have been so comforting for our European ancestors as the control measures for ergot did not start until 17th century France. Up until that time, one might say that the bread making was indeed the first unwitting LSD-like laboratory which unassumingly distributed its contents to the poor masses in regular doses at a fraction of the price for LSD. What the actual effects were then remain unknown, although it would be safe to say that the amounts were reduced, but not to the same extent as with modern control methods.

With the development of the scientific method and the microscope, the full life cycle of the ergot fungus was finally understood in the mid-19th century. Once corrective measures were implemented, ergot outbreaks became rarer in Europe with the last known convulsive outbreak occurring in Germany, Scandinavia, and Finland in the 19th century while Russia suffered extensively until 1926-1927. The decrease in European outbreaks occurred for many reasons including knowledge and understanding of the ergot fungi coupled with the implementation of appropriate control measures. Additionally, the rise of the international trade in grains, which required the standardization of grain quality, the implementation of agricultural practices aiming to minimize the spread of fungal spores, and also more effective food safety practices such as Hazard Analysis Critical Control Points (HACCP), all contributed to the decrease. Other controls now include planting cereal grains and forage grasses which are more resistant to the different strains of members of the Claviceps Genus. While European and Russian outbreaks are virtually non-existent today, reports of outbreaks in poorer countries have taken their place. The last known outbreak of convulsive ergotism was in India (1975) when 78 people experienced convulsions and other central nervous system (CNS) effects after eating grain infected with *C. fusiformis* fungus. The ergoline family, especially the ergotamine ergot chemical, was probably the culprit behind the psychosis. A few years later, Ethiopia experienced the last known outbreak of gangrenous ergotism when 47 people died from eating wild oats parasitized *with C. purpurea* and contaminated by the ergot chemicals ergotamine and ergometrine.

As has been noted by many through the centuries, ergot outbreaks always seemed to occur in the same area where rye was cultivated, something which was not elucidated until the 19th century. It was also noted that the outbreaks were limited to rural rather than urban areas in all affected countries. As much as the outbreak areas provide much useful information so too do the areas which experienced no outbreaks. Ergotism did not seem to affect people in southern Europe probably because the scletoria prefer cold winters followed by moist springs with temperatures 10-30ºC and high relative humidity. But spoiled or not, any food was consumed eagerly as it was in short supply during Europe's countless wars, variable weather impacting food production, inadequate post-harvest storage conditions, and many disease outbreaks. Many forensic, historical, and medical scientists have concluded that gangrenous ergotim occurred mostly west of the Rhine River while the convulsive type was prominent in northern Germany, Scandinavia, Eastern Europe, and Russia. The cause of this distinction still remains a mystery but the composition and concentrations of the pharmacologically active ergot chemicals is dependent on weather and soil conditions, different members of the Claviceps Genus including different strains of *C. purpurea*, and perhaps even also of the grain type. The 50 members of the Genus Claviceps infect economically important cereal and forage grasses including rye (the favourite "child"), wheat, triticale, barley, oats, corn, millet, rice, and sorghum. Most members of the Claviceps Genus are limited to infecting only a few grass species. However, there are exceptions, the major concern being *C. purpurea*, which coincidentally is the one that targets rye. This fungus is able to infect well over 300 cereal and forage grasses growing in open fields, moist forests, mountain habitats, and salt marshes. The needs of the *C. purpurea* are specific and the spores spread best under relatively cool and moist conditions. Although this can be partly explained by the fungus' life cycle, these climatic preferences have more to do with the life cycle of the host plants. Rye in particular, has flowers that open more frequently for longer periods of time when the weather is wet and cold. This exposes the reproductive organ of the flower to the airborne spores for greater periods of time, increasing the chances of infection. Soil that's moor and sandy also increases the probability of infection. From an agricultural perspective, factors such as tilled land, crops grown in rotation and an earlier harvest tend to decrease chances of infection. Although monitored closely by The World Health Organization (WHO) and by individual countries, the *Claviceps* spores are still able to rapidly cross international borders without a passport and traverse over large land masses, wide oceans, and tall mountains with ease. Affecting crops on all continents (except the Arctic and Antarctica), members of the *Claviceps* Genus remain on the international most wanted list as the object of close surveillance, intensive control, and untiring eradication. Modern technologies such as filtering systems have been employed in the prevention of ergotism due to *C.purpurea*. While these new methods have reduced the prevalence of infection, their removal of a large portion of healthy grains is a major drawback. As a result, much effort is dedicated to the development of improved rye cultivars that are entirely resistant to infection.

While *C. purpurea* is the most famous fungi which produce the bioactive ergot chemicals, other fungi of the Genera *Penicillium* and *Aspergillus* also have this notable ability. More than 40 different alkaloid chemicals (some of which belong to the same family as lysergic acid diethylamide - LSD) plus a variety of other chemicals have been isolated from members of the *Claviceps* Genus. The sclerotia of *C. purpurea* can have as much as 2% of its dry weight as chemicals that actively function within tissues with the average being 0.15-0.5% dry weight. It is known that as little as 0.1% can cause hallucinations and other psychotic disturbances.

Historically, it was probably the ergotamine and ergometrine chemicals in the scletoria which were behind the gangrenous expression of ergotism, while ergotamine and dihydroergotamine were responsible for the convulsive form. The pharmacological effects of the ergot chemicals have similar chemical structures to important brain neurotransmitters including serotonin, dopamine, and epinephrine causing a disruption in either their concentration levels or in their effective functioning. Originally, the ergotamine from ergot was the precursor in the first making of the psychedelic drug LSD which was highly popular during the drug crazed 60s. Lysergic acid diethylamide (LSD) and related chemicals interact with receptors in the brain which disrupts the activities of the neurotransmitter serotonin because of their similar structure. As serotonin is involved in the control of perceptual, regulatory, and behavioural areas in the brain, any disruption would cause distortions in one's sense of reality, sensory perception, and mood as well as in physiological functions such as hunger, body temperature, sexual behaviour, and muscle control. The LSD "trip" can either be mind-blowing, wondrous, or frightening depending upon the person's emotional state, which causes the person to see images, feel sensations, or even hear sounds which they would not otherwise have experienced. The mind is filled with psychedelic colours and images, and victims often see and talk to people not physically present. Some have even reported seeing snow in the hot month of July. People witnessing these events must think that the person is absolutely "crazy"! The manic behaviours of convulsive ergotism were usually followed by depression, which suggests that the serotonin supply has either been overused and can't be replaced, or that other chemicals are blocking its usage. The ergot chemical ergometrine prefers to bind to serotonin receptors on brain nerve cells, thereby inhibiting serotonin effects which could lead to depressive states. In gangrenous ergotism, ergometrine plays a role in causing constriction of blood vessels and thereby leading to poor blood supply of limb. The ergot chemical dihydroergotamine is derived from ergotamine and causes overstimulation of serotonin. As a result, the person experiences twitching and spasms in their muscles, changes in their mental state, hallucinations, sweating and fever. It also causes physical damage in an area of the spinal cord associated with convulsive ergotism. This confirms the post death reports from Medieval Europe which noted bleeding and softening of the brain and injuries in the same area of the brain as noted by modern investigators. Other ergot alkaloid chemicals have also been proposed to have different effects which may help to explain the symptoms of convulsive ergotism. An ergot chemical named bromocriptine affects the chemical glutamate, a neurotransmitter which causes a disassociation between what's seen by the senses and what's understood by the brain. Although scientists once thought bromocriptine enhanced the use of glutamate by the body, thereby adding to the serotonin "high", more recent evidence suggest that this chemical actually prevents its release and use. In other words, the role of glutamate is still unclear in the case of convulsive ergotism. This same chemical also interacts with the receptors of dopamine, another neurotransmitter in the brain, producing the effect of as much as a 400 fold increase in the release of dopamine. This would likely account for the increased feeling of euphoria as well as increased motivation, pleasure, and memory.

Even though the dosages required for convulsive ergotism seem to be much smaller compared to the gangrenous, small does not mean ineffective. While one large dose of ergot toxins would probably not produce any clinical effects, it was the small regular cumulative doses over a relatively short period of time that caused the outbreaks of the convulsive form. Compared to the gangrenous form, the convulsive form is caused by different ergot chemicals in different concentrations. The composition and concentration of the scletoria are also affected by a variety of environmental factors. When eaten, the ergot chemicals are only passively absorbed in the small intestine and into the blood (Hills, 2008). While they are absorbed poorly, the concentration needed to produce drug-like effects is extremely low as they can be very potent. Additionally, these convulsive ergot chemicals in their small amounts are able to easily cross into the brain, bypassing the barrier which protects the brain from most toxins. Likewise, the chemicals seem to persist in tissues and organs for longer periods of time, suggesting that they are either released from cells much more slowly than expected, and/or other chemicals may interfere with their release. It is believed that the severe convulsions are caused by the stimulation of the midbrain which causes exaggerated tendon reflexes. The ergot derivative with the greatest effect on the midbrain is a diethylamide derivative of LSD. The periods between the painful convulsions were often marked by low blood sugar which caused a voracious appetite.

Indeed, many chemicals extracted from plants and animals have much to contribute as they are valuable sources for not only drugs but also natural chemicals and colours used in food production. Approximately 25% of current drugs in Western medicine are plant based, with pharmaceutical companies digging deeper not only into historical records but also quite literally into remote forests as well as obtaining information from the indigenous peoples who have used them for generations. Nature is a treasure trove full of potential as it has created many different chemicals with different pharmacological effects for us to discover. Effective drugs have been produced from/with echinacea (purple cone flower), aspirin (acetylsalicylic acid (ASA), willow bark), caffeine (coffee), cocaine (coca leaves), digoxin, digitoxin, and digitalin (purple foxglove), lovastatin and mevastatin (fungi), marijuana (Cannabis plant), menthol (mint), nicotine (tobacco plants), opium and opiates such as morphine and codeine (opium poppy), penicillin (Penicillin fungus), etc, *etc.* And, more yet awaits!

The ergot outbreaks of the past have much to teach us and the chemicals still have much to show us. In the 16th century, the Renaissance physician and alchemist Paracelsus wrote "Everything is poison, there is poison in everything. Only the dose makes a thing not a poison" reflecting the often fine line between a chemical as a toxin or as a beneficial drug, with the ergot chemicals being prime examples. The earliest reports of the use of ergot as a medicine are from China (1100 B.C.) which describes its use to enhance labour. This was also later echoed in

Arabic medical writings with some evidence suggesting that Avicenna also used ergot infusions in his practice of medicine the 10th century, even writing a thesis on it. Whole ergot "grains" were deliberately harvested from rye fields as the chemicals quickly deteriorated in its powdered form. European midwives used this red powder routinely to make water-based infusions, but because only 20% of the chemicals are water soluble, the powder having unknown composition and concentration, and perhaps also the powder being old, the outcomes were unpredictable and sometimes fatal even when used for "appropriate" purposes. In the 19th century, a New York physician noted that this "pulvis ad partum" (powder of birth) had become "pulvis ad mortem" (powder of death) as it caused a substantial increase in the number of stillborn deaths after the recommendation for its regular use for in birthing by prominent physicians. Ergot was also used to treat the excruciating pain of migraine headaches with the first "official" use not occurring until the 19th century with grateful relieved sufferers in Italy, England, and the United States. The ergot scletoria became the unofficial source for effective migraine treatment although the identity of the causative agent remained unknown until the 1930s when purified ergotamine became available. In addition, ergot also contributed to its efficacy by its anti-serotonin effect. It remained so until medical science gained a better understanding of migraine headaches which lead to the development of other drugs such as sumatriptan in 1991.

There are no official records of ergot being deliberately used to induce hallucinations, although there are other fungi which cause hallucinations. The effects "magic mushrooms", or just "shrooms", have been known to mankind on every continent for millennia. Traditionally used in spiritual ceremonies, they are now consumed as a recreational drug. They are orally ingested either in a fresh or dry form and can be prepared in a number of ways. These "funny" mushrooms contain psilocybin which is a chemical that comes from mushrooms indigenous to the tropical and subtropical regions, such as South America and Mexico. Psilocybin is believed to alter concentrations of serotonin in the brain along with other chemicals, and can occur within twenty minutes of ingestion while lasting up to six hours in length. Once ingested, it is rapidly metabolized into the more hallucinogenic compound psilocin, which alters serotonin concentrations in the brain. This causes a peculiar alteration in one's perception of time and space as well as severe mood alterations. Although producing similar effects to LSD, psilocin is 200 times less potent, and the effects last for a shorter amount of time. The content of psilocin depends on the mushroom species in addition to other environmental factors, but usually ranges from 0.5-2% of its dry weight. Abusing psilocybin, which are generally done so by youths and young adults, has large risks that can result in fatal consequences if it is mistaken for another poisonous variety of mushrooms. Currently, there is no evidence that suggest psilocybin causes users to become dependent, but a tolerance may develop over time. The danger with these mushrooms has more to do with the misidentification which often results in many trips to emergency rooms every year. Euripedes, however, did not have any treatment for his wife and three children who fatally consumed toxic mushrooms in 430 B.C. Fresh or dried psilocybin containing mushrooms (whole or specific parts) are regulated in many countries and are also listed on the United Nations 1971 Convention on Psychotropic Substances, Schedule 1. The United States have various laws regarding the cultivation and possession of these mushrooms as legalities differ from state to state. In the United States, however, the North American Church, a large church of mainly indigenous peoples, is permitted by federal law to grow and to use their mushrooms in their religious ceremonies.

It's Monday after the holiday. Seeing your supervisor you give her the results of your secret three day mission which revealed that most of the grains had high in concentrations of ergot alkaloid whereas the flour analysis had 400-500 µg/kg which were below the levels of the European Union but above the German standard of 100 µg/kg. After reading your report, your supervisor breathes a sigh of relief and wipes the sweat from her forehead. "Good work, I am extremely happy and relieved by the results." Smiling, you leave to start working on the next sample already waiting for you on your workbench. While working, you cannot help but wonder about the ergot story... it caused so much suffering and yet it has given much, and still has more to give. The irony though is that the contaminated bread was the source of a disease which still affects so many people even to this day, despite concerted efforts to control it. At the same time too, bread was, and still continues to be, not only a source of life, prosperity, and health but also a very powerful symbol of God's blessings to the human race.

Glossary

Alkaloid: A group of substances that contain nitrogen and are naturally found in plants. Ergot alkaloids are chemicals of the alkaline nature found in ergot.

Aspergillus: A type of fungus comprised of numerous mould species capable of producing ergot chemicals. A large proportion of these organisms produce toxic substances while some cause food spoilage. They are widely used in the food industry in the creation of fermented foods.

Bromocriptine: An ergot chemical which is known to interact with glutamate and dopamine. It plays a role in convulsive ergotism.

Causative agent: Refers to a biological agent that causes disease.

Claviceps: A group of fungi that is present in rye, wheat, barley and oats. They produce toxic substances which can lead to ergostism.

Claviceps purpurea: (*C. purpurea*): A fungus present in rye which causes ergotism.

Convulsive Ergotism: The result of ergot poisoning which leads to hallucinations and convulsive seizures.

Cuneiform Tablet: One of the earliest forms of writing, cuneiform was invented in Uruk, Mesopotamia around 3000 BC. The word is from Latin, meaning "wedge-shaped". The symbols are formed from wedge-shaped objects pressed into soft clay tablets.

Dihydroergotamine: An ergot chemical compound that causes constriction of blood vessels through stimulation of several types of receptors.

Dopamine: A neurotransmitter released in the brain which has an inhibitory effect on movement. It is believed to be involved in mood and thought disorders and in abnormal movement disorders such as Parkinson's disease.

Epinephrine: Also known as adrenaline, it stimulates the nervous system in response to stress and other stimuli. It makes the heart beat faster and can raise blood pressure.

Ergometrine: An ergot chemical produced by Ergot fungus *Claviceps purpurea*. It has a chemical structure similar to LSD. It causes food poisoning when food contaminated with it is consumed. It is used in the medical field to control bleeding after child birth (Ergot: A group of fungi of the genus *Claviceps* that grows on rye and related plants.

Ergotamine: A chemical derived from the ergot fungus Claviceps purpurea. It may cause food poisoning in food contaminated with ergot which has not been eliminated via cleaning and milling. It can be destroyed by cooking.

Ergotism: The long term effects of ergot poisoning from the mould *Claviceps purpurea*. The effects of poisoning are either of the convulsive form or the gangrenous form.

Gangrenous Ergotism: Refers to a disease which causes tissue death by constricting the blood vessels leading to the extremities. Because of the decrease in blood flow, infections occur in the extremities, accompanied by burning pain. Once tissue death has occurred, the fingers, toes, *etc.* become mummified, and will eventually fall off as a result of infection. If the infected extremities are not removed, infection can spread further up the extremity that has been infected. Gangrenous ergotism is common in grazing farm animals but also occurs in humans.

Genus: A level of classification used to group living organisms. It is a broader term than "species". Plural: Genera.

Glutamate: A salt of glutamic acid. In addition to being one of the 20 major amino acids which make up proteins, it is a major excitatory signal of the central nervous system.

Grain Beating: To separate the seeds from the stem of a cereal grain by beating with a flail or by machine. Also referred to as threshing.

HACCP (Hazard Analysis Critical Control Points): Standards established by the government in order to increase food safety in the food industry. A HACCP plan includes identification of physical, biological and chemical hazards in key processing steps where these hazards may be introduced.

Hermetically Sealed: Any container having an airtight seal.

Ignis Sacer: An immediate or chronic intoxication resulting from ingestion of grain infected with ergot fungus, or from continuous use of drugs containing ergot.

LSD (Lysergic Acid Diethylamine): An illicit drug which causes hallucination, distorting perception, judgement and thinking. It increases serotonin activity as well as stimulates dopamine receptors in the body.

Midbrain: A part of the brain located at the back of the head near the neck. It acts as a relay station for visual and auditory information.

Mycotoxicosis: Poisoning caused by ingestion of mycotoxins. Symptoms often include difficulty breathing, nausea and headaches.

Mycotoxins: Secondary products produced by fungi that can cause disease and fatality in humans and animals.

Neurotransmitter: Secreted by nerve cells which passes messages to target cells in response to stimulation.

Non-Photosynthetic: A plant or species that does not use light to obtain energy.

Oxidized: Combined with or having undergone a chemical reaction with oxygen.

Penicillium: similar to Aspergillus, this group of fungi also has the ability to produce ergot chemicals. It is related to penicillin which is derived from this group of fungi.

Psilocin: A drug that acts to mimic the symptoms of psychosis. It is related chemically to psilocybin.

Psilocybin: A drug that generates hallucinations and an active ingredient of various Mexican hallucinogenic mushrooms of the genus Psilocybe Mexicana. It can produce altered states of mood and consciousness and has no acceptable medical use in the United States.

Sclerotium: A compact mass of hardened fungi with reserve food material that in some higher fungi becomes detached and remains dormant until a favourable opportunity for growth occurs. Usually purple in colour and contains mycotoxins. Plural: sclerotia.

Serotonin: Also known as 5-hydroxytryptamine. A hormone found in plant, animals and humans. It is derived from the amino acid, tryptophan. It functions to constrict blood vessels and acts as a neurotransmitter in the body.

Sieving: The act of separating solids from liquids using a sieve (plastic or metal mesh frame). It may also be used to separate particle of various sizes by changing the tightness or closeness of the mesh framework.

Sumatriptan: refers to a drug that is used for treating migraine headaches. It belongs to a class of drugs called selective serotonin receptor agonists.

WHO (World Health Organization): Global organization top priorities include the reduction of deaths caused by disasters and to improve health care for preventable diseases. They also provide statistics for any health-related epidemics and provide standards in order to prevent future occurrences.

References

Bennett, J. W.; Klinch, M. 2003. Mycotoxins. Clinical Microbiology Reviews. 16, 497-516.

Best, C L.; Acierno, R. E.; Resnick, H .S. 2003. Psilocybin Fast Facts. United States.

Coppock, R. W.; and Jacobsen, B. J. 2009. Mycotoxins in animal and human patients. *Toxicology and Industrial Health*. 25(9-10), 637-655.

Eadie, M. J. 2003. Convulsive ergotism: epidemics of the serotonin syndrome? *Lancet Neurology*, 2, 249-34.

Fung, F.; and Clark, R. F. 2004. Health Effects of Mycotoxins: A Toxicological Overview. *Clinical Toxicology*, 42(2), 217-234.

Gillman, K. 2010. Triptans, Serotonin Agonists, and Serotonin Syndrome (Serotonin Toxicity): *A Review. American Headache Society*, 50, 264-272.

Halberstadt, A. L.; Geyer, M. A. 2011. Multiple receptors contribute to the behavioral effects of indoleamine hallucinogens. *Neuropharmacology*, 61, 364-381.

Hill, N .S. 2008. Absorption of Ergot Alkaloids in the Ruminant. In "Neotyphodium in Cool-Season Grasses," eds. C. A. Roberts, C. P. West and D. E. Spiers.pp.271-290. Blackwell Publishing Ltd, Oxford, UK.

Kainulainen, K. 2003. Ergot and ergot alkaloids, a review. Uppsala University.

Krska, R.; Stubbings, G.; Macarthur, R.; and Crews, C. 2008. Simultaneous determination of six major ergot alkaloids and their epimers in cereals and foodstuffs by LC–MS–MS. *Analytical and Bioanalytical Chemistry*, 391, 563-576.

Lee, M. R. 2009. The history of ergot of rye (*Claviceps purpurea*) I From antiquity to 1900. *Journal of the Royal College of Physicians of Edinburgh*, 39, 179-184.

Mulac, D.; Humpf, H-U. 2011. Cytotoxicity and accumulation of ergot alkaloids in human primary cells. *Toxicology,* 282, 112-121.

Müller, C.; Kemmlein, S.; Klaffke, H.; Krauthause, W.; Preib-Weigert,A.; and Wittkowski, R. 2009. Research article-A basic tool for risk assessment: A new method for the analysis of ergot alkaloids in rye and selected rye products. *Molecular Nutrition and Food Research*, 53, 500-507.

Scott, P. M. 2007. An analysis of ergot - A review. *Mycotoxin Research*, 23(3), 113-121.

Shirasaki, Y.; Sugimura, M.; Sato, T. 2010. Bromocriptine, an ergot alkaloid, inhibits excitatory amino acid release mediated by glutamate transporter reversal. *European Journal of Pharmacology*, 643(1), 48-57.

Smith, D.; Schwartz, R. 1988. Hallucinogenic Mushrooms. *Clinial Pediatrics*, 27(2), 70-73. Retrieved from the Scholars Portal database.

Speijers, G.; Alink, G.; Saeger, S.; Hardy, A.; Magan, N.; Pilegaard, K.; Battilani, P.; Riemens, M. 2010. Evaluation of Agronomic Practices for Mitigation of Natural Toxins. *International Life Sciences Institute*, 14-16.

Suissa, S.; Haverkamp, W.; Garbe, E. 2007. Dopamine agonists and the risk of cardiac-valve regurgitation. *New England Journal of Medicine*, 356, 29-38.

Yamashita, H.; Kawakami, H.; Zhang, Y.X.; Tanaka, K.; Nakamura, S. 1997. Effect of amino acid ergot alkaloids on glutamate transport via human glutamate transporter hGluT-1. *Journal of Neurological Sciences*, 155, 31-36.

§9:

The Unreturnable 'Gifts' of the 'Dream Fish'

While flavour tripping with Miracle berries in order to 'fool' the brain is a deliberate conscious choice causing pleasurable mind altering experiences, other more dramatic and bizarre psychoactive events can be involuntary as they can be caused during the consumption of ordinary everyday foods. While certainly rare, these hallucinogenic experiences are sporadic and unpredictable during the spring and summer months as some ocean and coastal water fish eat large amounts of naturally poisoned food during their early rapid growth phase.

Imagine driving along the coastline of the blue Mediterranean Sea on a warm, sunny day. Being on vacation, you decide to stop at a little seaside town for lunch. Wandering into a restaurant at lunchtime, you ask for the local specialty, a fish platter consisting of *Sarpa salpa*. After enjoying the delicious satisfying lunch, you continue your drive listening to the Beatles singing "Lucy in the sky with diamonds", a popular 1960s song with strange lyrics and with even stranger images. The song sparks thoughts of a turbulent decade of counter culture, social revolution, and recreational drug use, especially psychedelic drugs such as LSD which was the drug of choice by the 'hippie' generation who sought alternative forms of enlightenment while challenging many of society's conventions and taboos. This era symbolized by flower power, psychedelic images, and very bright 'in your face' colours could be summarized by the infamous slogan, 'Turn on, tune in, drop out'. Soon after your fishy lunch, you start to feel strange. All of a sudden strange sounds seem to come from nowhere, your car is attacked by a giant squid … uncertainty strikes … you literally drop out for about 36 hours! The hallucinogenic properties of compounds sometimes found in this member of the Sea Bream family can lead to some unbelievable magical tours with accompanying visions of demonic animals, giant anthropoids, crippling terror and unearthly howls.

Waking up, you have no recollection of the past two days but you learn that you were indeed awake. You begin to wonder how one could be awake yet not remember even one single thing. Unbeknownst to you, you got more than you bargained for with the fish lunch … the 'added bonus' was a case of ichthyoallyeinotoxism (Greek, *ichthus*-fish, *aleuin*-to be out of oneself, *i.e.* hallucinate, and *toxikon*-venom), a rare and poorly understood fish borne intoxication. This long word is almost as bad as the fish poisoning you experienced a type of hallucinogenic poisoning caused by eating the head and internal organs of members of the Sea Bream family such as certain mullets, goatfish, tangs, damsels, rabbit fish, and *S. salpa* which consume phytoplankton and algae as natural parts of their diet. Other species from the *Kyphosus* genus can also cause ichthyoallyeinotoxism. It has been shown that some of these species have bufotenine in their skin, a substance which can cause hallucinations as well. Another genus member the *Siganus spinus*, is another potentially hallucinogenic fish which is commonly referred to as the "fish that inebriates" by the Mascareignes. In some the Hawaiian Islands there is a fish which is called *Mulloidichthys samoensis*, translated as "the chief of ghosts," due to its ability to produce hallucinations.

There are a variety of different fish used for human consumption; however some fish have side effects when consumed such as poisoning. There are different types of fish-induced poisoning; the most common type affects the peripheral nervous system- the system of nerves that are not located in the brain or spinal cord. The type of poisoning caused by Sea Bream species, however, affects the central nervous system- the nerves of the brain and spinal cord. The results of this kind of fish-induced poisoning cause the nerves on the brain to misfire and as a result the person experiences the touch, sound, taste, smell or sight of things that aren't actually there. These hallucinations show up usually the night that the poisoned fish is eaten, but are not the first symptoms to show up. Within 2 hours of eating nausea, vomiting, muscle weakness, loss of balance and blurry vision can be present; this is followed by the hallucinations. These symptoms tend to last less than 36 hours but muscle weakness can remain for up to 3 days.

Sea Bream fish occupy many of the world's tropical waters, as a result Sea Bream fish-induced poisoning occurs mainly in the Mediterranean Sea, Indian and Pacific Ocean areas. There are eight families of toxic species, most of which consist of plankton-eating and scavenging fish along the coastal areas. Human poisoning is dependent upon a variety of circumstances including where the fish is caught, the time of year and how the fish is prepared for eating. Poisoning is the result of a microorganism called *Gambierdiscus toxicus* that lives within the fish's flesh and gut. The microorganism is not easily destroyed by heat and can survive even after the fish has been fully cooked. It has been reported that poisoning and hallucinations occur less often in fall and winter months, because algae growth is slower during this time, and if the fish have their heads and guts removed prior to cooking. Although these conditions lessen the chances of a possible hallucination or poisoning the risk of either is always present when consuming any kind of Sea Bream.

Hallucinatory experiences have existed since the beginning of mankind. Hallucinations were once seen as either angelic or demonic, but essentially thought of as a super power that was diverted from a higher power source. Until the 19th century, with the development of modern science and proper medical education, hallucinations were usually seen as a form of mental illness.

A hallucination can be explained as the brain's reception of false sensory inputs. In a stricter sense, it can be defined as perceptions in a conscious and awake state with the absence of external stimuli. In this sense, patients have a vivid and realistic sensory experience that may take them into an alternate state of reality. A hallucination is sometimes confused with similar or related phenomena such as dreaming, illusions or Pseudo hallucinations.

There are many causes of hallucinations. Physical illness such as high fever, sleep deprivation and tumours can cause false perceptions in our body's sensory system. More common and familiar causes are psychoses such as Schizophrenia, depression or when one is under extreme stress. Hallucinations are also possible with the use of hallucinogenic drugs and/or alcohol intoxication. Hallucinations can also occur during withdrawal from alcohol or addictive drugs as the body is under extreme stress during this time of physical and chemical change.

Hallucinations can be classified into different categories based on which of our five senses it affects. The most common type hallucination is auditory, which is the perception of sound without any outside stimulus. It is usually divided into two categories: elementary and complex. Elementary auditory hallucinations typically involve sounds of hissing, whistling, walking, and knocking on doors *etc.* On the other hand, complex auditory hallucinations involve the perception of more complex sounds such as voices and music.

Visual hallucination is another common type of hallucination. In this case patients see images that are not present or do not reconcile with reality. These can be caused by both psychotic disorders or as an effect of drug and alcohol related illness. Visual hallucinations can also be caused by an overwhelming imagination. Other types of hallucinations, although less common, are olfactory, gustatory and tactile. Olfactory hallucination involves smelling odours that are not present and are usually unpleasant to our senses. Gustatory hallucinations are quite similar to olfactory hallucinations in that they involve the perception of non-existing tastes, again, which are typically unpleasant. Finally there are tactile hallucinations. These are illusions of physical sensory input simulating various types of pressure to the skin or other organs. One of the most common is the feeling of insects crawling on ones' skin. Researchers have discovered that in many cases the root causes of olfactory and gustatory hallucinations are not typically from mental instability, but are actually side effects from physically unwell bodies.

Other scientific findings have also suggested that hallucinations are not that uncommon in the general population. Many prescription drugs while mostly prescribed for other reasons can cause hallucinogenic effects whereas other drugs, some illegal, are self-prescribed and administered for a variety of reasons. Surprisingly, common and uncommon foods too such as Stilton cheese, Sea Bream, and nutmeg also contain substances which can cause hallucinogens but these foods are consumed for their nutritive rather than psychoactive effects. A recent report based on self-evaluation and interview surveys concluded that the frequency of hallucinations in the general public is 5-8%, which is considerably greater than what had previously been considered. This can be due to the increase stress in the modern life style as well as the increasing abuse of hallucinogenic drugs and alcohol. Scientists have even suggested that hallucinations could be a "by-product" of human evolution and therefore a natural part of life.

When it comes to investigating the hallucinations caused by members of the Sea Bream family it is important to understand this marine animal's background. All species of sea bream have a relatively similar look: a fairly tall but thin, flat body. These fish are omnivores mostly, feeding on crustaceans, crayfish, oysters, mussels, small fish, worms, algae and plankton. Sea Bream fish are highly versatile and live in an abundance of regions throughout the world. They are very adaptable and can be found in both temperate and tropical waters and can be found in open seas, as well as inshore areas such as mangroves. They can travel in large numbers in estuaries-- semi-closed bodies of water that connect rivers to open oceans; as well is in brackish and fresh water. In most environments, sea breams like to seek shelter in sea grass beds, reefs and rocks. Depending on the species of sea bream, they are found in different locations. The Black Sea Bream is common throughout the waters surrounding the southern United Kingdom, while the Western Atlantic Sea Bream occupies the Atlantic Ocean from the waters of New Jersey down to Argentina. The Red Sea Bream is often found off the shores of China and Japan, and the *Sarpa salpa* is commonly found in South Africa, the Mediterranean and in the waters surrounding Australia and India.

Due to the sea breams commonality throughout the world, they are both a popular sport fishing animal as well as a substantial source of food. They have strong teeth that make them a slight challenge to fishermen looking to sport fish, but they have a mild taste and tender white meat making them a delicious and popular food source.

According to Oliver Crimmen, a fish curator at the National History Museum, the plankton contains very small amounts of a poison which develops sporadically and unpredictably during the convergence of unknown seasonal and regional phenomena. Growing rapidly, Sea Bream such as *S. salpa* eat a great deal of it during their early life causing its accumulation in the brain as well as other internal organs but the reason for this partition of the poison in these tissues is a mystery. As this toxin is heat stable it is not inactivated or destroyed when the fish is cooked. But upon consuming *S. salpa*, the poison acts as a neurotoxin as it primarily causes various psychoactive CNS manifestations. But according to Crimmen, only certain types of plankton accumulate this toxin, and hence eating this fish will not usually produce psychoactive effects in all cases. If one is so unfortunate (or lucky) to consume *S. salpa*, they will experience some of the most intense and long-lasting psychoactive symptoms known to be caused by a food intoxication.

The cause of ichthyoallyeinotoxism, a type of hallucinogenic fish intoxication poisoning, is presently not completely understood as cases are rare, under reported for various reasons, and resolved within 36-72 hours after fish consumption. With the few reported cases, it has been noted that the toxicity of the poison is dependent on fishing location, season, and also method preparation with most poisonings occurring in Mediterranean during the spring and summer. It has been suggested that this phenomenon may be due to global warming as the sea temperatures increase sufficiently to not only nurture increased and rapid plankton and algae growth but also the presence of non-traditional native fish.

Food poisoning from fish and seafood is very common since they are an important source of protein, essential minerals, vitamins A and B and unsaturated fatty acids that individuals need to live a healthy life. Generally, food poisoning associated with fish and seafood can be categorized as infection or intoxication. Infection involves the consumption of fish contaminated by pathogens such as bacteria, viruses, or parasites. Note that this form of food poisoning involves the actual consumption of live and viable pathogens. After the pathogens are consumed, they enter the intestines, multiply and produce toxins that infect the body. Symptoms of this type of food poisoning arise usually within 24 hours as the infection takes time to develop. These symptoms include abdominal pain, diarrhea, and vomiting. Furthermore, pathogens can move from the intestines into other organs and tissues resulting in additional symptoms, depending on the area of infection, and fever. One example of infection by fish is cause by the pathogen fishborne zoonotic trematodes (flukes). This infection is the result of the consumption of raw or inadequately cooked fish. This pathogen will live and develop into adult in the host's intestines. Specifically, liver flukes will cause infection leading to liver cancer, cholangitis, and pancreatitis.

Intoxication on the other hand is from the ingestion of toxin and requires no live or viable cells. The toxin can be chemical (*i.e.* mercury) or a biotoxin produced by pathogens and microorganisms (*i.e.* bacteria, algae). Symptoms of this type of food poisoning occur within just a short time after consumption of the toxin (can be as short as 30 minutes). Intoxication requires only a small amount of toxin to induce symptoms and illnesses. Microbial toxins include enterotoxins and neurotoxins. Enterotoxins cause gastric symptoms. An example of enterotoxins is Staphylococcal toxin - one of the most common causes of food poisoning. Neurotoxins induce neurological symptoms. Examples of neurotoxins include ciguatoxin (which actually induces both gastrointestinal and neurological symptoms) and tetrodotoxin. Symptoms of intoxication by neurotoxins are blurred vision, difficulty in swallowing, breathing and talking and paralysis of involuntary muscles which can result in death.

Ichthyoallyetinotoxism is a type of hallucinogenic fish intoxication. Symptoms of this type of intoxication appear shortly after toxin consumption and victims usually recover with 36 to 72 hours. Ichthyoallyetinotoxism is wide spread in areas near the Indian and Pacific Ocean as well as the Mediterranean Sea. The occurrence of this intoxication depends on the season as well as the location. Little is known about this intoxication but this toxin is believed to be heat stable, as cases after consumption of fish prepared by either being fried, boiled or steamed have been observed. Eight families of fish have been reported to be associated with ichthyoallgeinotoxism. They include Magilidae (such as mullet) and serranidae (such as Coral Grouper/Rockcod) from the Indo-Pacific Ocean and Saridae (such as the Sea Bream) from the Mediterranean area.

Foodborne illnesses are defined as diseases, either infectious or toxic in nature, resulting from the consumption of contaminated food, pathogenic bacteria, viruses, or parasites that contaminate food. Both raw and processed fish and shellfish can cause food poisoning since they feed on plankton and algae contaminated with naturally produced toxins. Plankton and algae are plants that produce natural toxins that are intended for guarding against specific threats by predators or disease, such as hungry insects or damaging fungus. Some of these toxins are produced naturally by plants and could cause illness in humans if they were concentrated at high levels and were consumed in large quantities.

The first intoxication that may occur is Ciguatera food poisoning syndrome which arises due to the consumption of these types of fish: moray eel, red snapper, grouper, and sea bass. Historically restricted to tropical and sub-tropical regions, hot spots are in the Caribbean islands and south Florida. This poison does not go away when the fish is cooked or frozen with symptoms of ciguatera poisoning including abdominal cramps, nausea, vomiting and diarrhea. Symptoms can then progress to headache, muscle aches, itchy skin, numbness or tingling. The name of the poison that causes ciguatera is ciguatoxin. Ciguatoxin affects our body's peripheral nervous system (PNS) which includes all the nerves in our bodies excluding those in the brain and spinal cord, known as the central nervous system (CNS). The main function of our peripheral nervous system is to connect the central nervous system to our limbs and organs. The ciguatoxin inhibits this connection between the PNS and CNS and can even send false messages between the two which accounts for odd, involuntary behaviour within the victim's body. The misfiring of nerve signals is dangerous and can cause a number of unwanted symptoms. Paralysis, heart contraction and the inability to hear or detect temperature are just a few common outcomes. The symptoms of ciguatera are only physical because of the fact that the ciguatoxin cannot cross our body's blood brain barrier. The blood brain barrier (BBB) is a physiological mechanism that alters the permeability of brain capillaries, so that some substances, such as certain drugs or toxins, are prevented from entering brain tissue while other substances such as oxygen and nutrients are allowed to enter freely. Certain toxins, referred to as neurotoxins, do have the special ability to cross this protective barrier to our brains and causes detrimental damage. We will be discussing this further in the third type of fish intoxication, tetrodotoxin.

The second type of seafood poisoning that can occur is Scombroid poisoning. This illness results from consumption of spoiled fish. It is most commonly reported with mackerel, tuna, mahi-mahi, bonito, sardines, anchovies, and related species of fish that were inadequately refrigerated or preserved after being caught. A substance called histamine naturally builds up in some fish when they get too warm after being caught and at high levels they can produce toxic effects. Usually when histamine enters our bodies it is harmless and is a chemical that serves as an alarm to let your immune system know that an infection is attacking part of the body. It becomes dangerous when we consume a large amount of histamine at one time, as in eating a meal of spoiled seafood. Often victims of scombroid poisoning do not know that they are suffering from this illness because its symptoms are similar to a common allergic reaction. These symptoms of poisoning can show within just minutes, and up to two hours, following consumption and can range from minor to severe. Minor symptoms include: facial flushing/sweating, burning-peppery taste sensations in the mouth and throat, dizziness, nausea, headache, hives and abdominal cramps. These symptoms usually last for approximately four to six hours and rarely exceed one to two days. In severe cases of scombroid poisoning, hazardous physical effects such as: blurred vision, respiratory stress and swelling of the tongue can occur. Treatment for scombroid poisoning is similar to any other allergic reaction. The administration of water and oxygen is important as well as anti-histamine such as Benadryl which will provide relief from the minor allergy-like symptoms. Scrombroid poisoning is 100% preventable through the proper handling and storage of fresh fish. You can avoid the risk of contracting this food-borne illness by ensuring that you buy your fish and seafood from a reputable market or restaurant.

The third and final type of fish intoxication is called Tetrodotoxin which is considered to be the most lethal toxin coming from the marine environment and therefore causes the most severe kind of seafood poisoning. Anhydrotetrodotoxin 4-epitetrodotoxin, better known as Tetrodotoxin is a toxin that is 10,000 times more lethal than cyanide and is perhaps the most potent toxin present in nature. Tetrodotoxin is most famously present in the puffer fish but other animals can contain traces of it as well. The blue-ringed octopus, harlequin frogs, and rough-skinned newts are among the few species that naturally contain this toxin. The toxin is variously used in these animals as a defensive biotoxin to ward off predation, or as both defensive and predatory venom. It especially concentrates in the skin and gonads of fish, amphibians, or reptile, and in the intestine, liver of mollusks. These particular organs accumulate large amounts of heavy metal or other ingested toxic substances. Tetrodotoxin has even been isolated from certain strains of algae, along with more marine life such as some snails, crabs and even a type of flatworm. Consumption of the toxin usually occurs in the regions of Asia or the Pacific Islands but is not isolated to those areas as the contaminated fish meat can be shipped overseas, cooked and consumed while still containing a lethal amount of tetrodotoxin. Symptoms of this fish poisoning typically develop within 30 minutes of ingestion, but may be delayed by up to four hours. Often there is a progression to these symptoms with the first symptom of intoxication being a slight numbness of the lips and tongue. The next symptom is increasing tingling in the face and extremities, which may be followed by sensations of lightness or floating. Headache, abdominal pain, nausea, diarrhea, and/or vomiting may occur. Occasionally, difficulty in walking may occur. The second stage of the intoxication is increasing paralysis making it difficult for victims to move, speak and even breathe. As paralysis increases convulsions, mental impairment, and cardiac arrhythmia may occur. The victim, although completely paralyzed, may be conscious and in some cases completely lucid until shortly before death. Death usually occurs within 4 to 6 hours. If the patient survives 24 hours, then recovery without any residual effects will usually occur over several days. There is no known antidote for tetrodotoxin poisoning and treatment is often symptomatic and can consist of emptying the stomach, feeding the victim activated charcoal to bind the toxin, and taking standard life-support measures to keep the victim alive until the effect of the poison has worn off. The best way to avoid the toxin tetrodotoxin is to not consume any marine life in the order of Tetraodontiformes. A good rule of thumb to live by is that if the fish is brightly coloured that is a warning sign from nature saying "stay away I am poisonous!"

Every year a number of people in Japan are poisoned by eating raw puffer fish (*aka* fugu) especially in the winter months when the tetrodotoxin is at the highest levels. Puffer's poisoning causes deadening of the tongue and limps, dizziness, vomiting, rapid heart rate, difficulty breathing, and muscle paralysis. Most of the victims die within 4 to 24 hours after this toxin has been consumed. While deliberately sought out and consumed by many people for its tingling effects, just a pinhead amount of this highly potent toxin can cause victims to die from suffocation as diaphragm muscles are paralyzed. From the descriptions in the ship's log, it is believed that Captain Cook and his crew experienced two separate incidents of puffer fish poisoning in 1774 during their exploration of the southwest Pacific Ocean. Not only can fish intoxications be serious and fatal, so too can fish infections but not directly. Some native peoples living in northern Canada or Alaska unknowingly contract botulism every year which is caused by the incorrect fermentation of their fish. While treatable, the infection is usually fatal in such remote places as medical assistance is usually far away.

While fish intoxications such as scombroid and tetrodotoxin are caused by the presence of naturally present substances in the fish, both ciguatera intoxication and ichthyoallyeinotoxism are caused the consumption of specific fish which have feed on toxic phytoplankton and algae. The fish intoxication resulting from the consumption of Sea Bream members such as *S. salpa* is probably the most extreme with all the different CNS psychoactive symptoms including visual and auditory hallucinations often including unusual animals, delirium, nightmares, feelings of imminent death, and depression. Other symptoms include feelings of chest constriction which can begin only a few hours after eating the delicious fish but all these symptoms usually are self-limited to three or four days.

Currently, the causative agent of the hallucinations by from Sea Bream consumption is under debate, and how it actually causes the hallucinations is still not understood. It has been hypothesized that the hallucinogenic properties originate from the alkaloids of the indole groups which have many chemical structural similarities to LSD. While the non-toxic compound has only one indole branch, the psychotropic version has two such branches. While almost all fish consume at some phytoplankton or algae as part of their diet, it is only those fish which consume the algae containing this specific chemical that will cause psychoactive effects. Since the psychoactive compound in the Sea Bream fish is derived from the identical base as LSD, it is tentatively assumed that the dosage required to produce psychoactive effects would be similar to that of LSD. The oral dose needed to produce psychic phenomena from LSD is 0.5 to 1.0 milligrams per kilogram of weight (mg/kg) whereas the clinical dose used by some psychotherapists is 1.0-2.0 mg/kg which is 70-140 mg for a 70 kg person.

The positive identity of the toxin in *S. salpa* remain unknown and can only be inferred from supportive circumstantial evidence as the reported intoxications are few with no obtainable physical evidence. It has been shown that some members of the green algae *Caulerpaceae microalgaes* contain a toxin in its green clusters which resemble green grapes called caulerpin, an alkaloid chemical with two indole branches. This toxin appears to be a neurotoxin having a molecular multi-ring chemical structure with two indole chains, giving it a 3-D structure similar to LSD. This toxin is believed to originate from the phytoplankton *Gambierdiscus toxicus,* and it is quite possible that the algae can be contaminated with this toxin as a deteriorating marine environment fosters the rapid growth of this phytoplankton. Further evidence supporting this identification is provided by the Philippine people who normally consume the algae but avoid it during the rainy season as it believed to be toxic. In terms of physical and psychoactive effects caulerpin has some effects to similar serotonin, a stimulative neurotransmitter. It is known that seeds detoxify themselves from ammonia accumulation by storing the ammonia in the 'indole' part of the amino acid L-tryptophan and through a series of reactions the ammonia is metabolized into serotonin. L-tryptophan is just an amino acid that is derived from plant or animal sources; it has been used in alternative medicine as an aid to treat sleep problems, anxiety, depression, and other harmful conditions. It is hypothesized that serotonin's presence in seeds is to speed up transit time through the GI tract as serotonin can cause diarrhea, and an increased amount of free serotonin in the blood can induce vomiting probably as a defensive mechanism but these two are usually not part of *S. salpa* intoxication. In its native bioactive form serotonin is not able to cross the blood-brain barrier. The blood brain barrier makes certain exceptions for allowing passage of molecules to the brain tissue this is why a form of serotonin found in many plant leaves is absorbed across the blood-brain barrier and can cause hallucinations. Interestingly the classic psychedelic drug ecstasy (*aka* 3,4-methylenedioxymethamphetamine (MDMA)) also acts by the same serotonin receptors producing their classical hallucinogenic effects. But, the symptoms of either a serotonin overdose or caulerpin intoxication is very dissimilar to the symptoms caused by eating *S. salpa*. The toxic syndrome from eating these fish is more like ciguatera fish intoxication and has often been confused with it. But not all members in the Sea Bream family and certainly not all *S. Salpa* are toxic but it seems that only those which have consumed sufficient amounts of this specific algae contaminated with caulerpin with its two 'indole' groups which are probably responsible for the hallucinogenic effects. While caulerpin has a low toxicity in humans, the concentration of this heat stable toxin in the heads and other internal organs many just be sufficient to produce its psychoactive effects. The reason for the concentrating effect in these particular tissues is unknown, perhaps being a sequestrating mechanism. It known that such toxin concentration also occurs in other toxic fish such as the puffer fish where it is found in the reproductive organs as well as the flesh as well as in various tissues of many plants.

In conclusion, the reported symptoms of S. *salpa* intoxication is stimulative not depressive and this phenomenon would be in agreement with the observation that seaweeds predominantly have toxins with CNS stimulant activity, not depressive. Whatever the identity of this heat stable toxin, it is able to cross the blood-brain barrier as well as concentrate in other organs, having some commonalities with LSD, serotonin, and caulerpin.

While the psychoactive effect caused by unknowingly consuming poisoned members of the Sea Bream family is only temporary, the experience can nonetheless be mind blowing, and is probably not most people's list of 100 things to do in a lifetime. It could be said, however, that on these bad fish trips (no pun intended), one usually wants the legendary fish to get away.

Tripping on sea bream is definitely not for the faint of heart.

Glossary

Action potential: is a short-lasting event in which the electrical membrane potential of a cell rapidly rises and falls. It represents rapid reversals in voltage across the plasma membrane of axons.

Algae: Non-flowering stem less water-plants more commonly known as seaweed and plankton.

Alkaloids: Chemical compounds containing the element nitrogen, from plant origin, *e.g.* morphine.

Antidote: Any chemical compound that can be used to oppose or neutralize the effects of a toxin (based on Dorland's Medical Dictionary).

Biotoxin: A type of biological agent; often a poison produced by plants, bacteria and other organisms that are highly toxic for other organisms.

Blood-brain barrier: The barrier separating circulatory blood from the brain's extracellular fluid. The barrier of cells alters the permeability (penetration potential) of the brain's capillaries so that some substances are allowed to permeate freely, while others are not.

Bufotenine: An alkaloid (see alkaloid) found in the skin of some species of toads; in mushrooms, higher plants, and mammals that can cause hallucinations (*cf.* hallucination).

Caulerpin: An alkaloid (see alkaloid) toxin (see toxin) with two indole (see indole) branches.

Central nervous system: The centre of the body's network of nerve cells.

Cholangitis: The inflammation of the bile ducts. I is most commonly cause by a bacterial infection.

Ciguatera: A disease caused by the consumption of tropical fish that feed on toxin-(see toxin) producing algae (see algae).

Ciguatoxin- a seafood toxin that is acquired by eating fish that have consumed toxic single-celled marine organisms or fish that have consumed other fish that have become toxic.

Depolarization: Is a change in a cell's membrane potential, making it more positive, or less negative. May result in an action potential.

Depression: A mood disorder marked especially by sadness, inactivity, difficulty with thinking and concentration, a significant increase or decrease in appetite and time spending sleeping, feeling of dejection and hopeless, and sometimes suicidal thoughts or an attempt to commit suicide.

Dreaming: Does not involve wakefulness.

Enterotoxins: A toxin released by pathogens in the intestines which affects the gastrointestinal tract causing diarrhea, vomiting, and abdominal pain.

External stimuli: Something around you that triggers you to do something, or to response to the environment.

Enzymes: Biological catalysts that help to speed up a chemical reaction by reducing its activation energy without being used up in the reaction.

Food Infection: An illness resulting from ingesting food containing a large amounts of harmful microorganisms, toxic man-made chemicals, or other deleterious substances, usually causing an upset of the digestive system.

Food Intoxication: A foodborne illness due to ingestion of food contaminated with microorganisms that have produced a toxin in the food (Textbook).

Hallucination: An experience involving the apparent perception of something that is not present. The human mind can not properly distinguish reality. Hallucinogenic drugs often cause a hallucination.

Heat stable: A compound (usually a protein) that is able to keep its shape in three dimensions and remain functional after exposure to high temperature conditions.

Ichthycallyeinotoxin (Ichthyoallyeinotoxism): also called "Hallucinogenic fish poisoning", caused by eating certain tropical fish. The species most commonly claimed to be capable of producing this kind of toxicity include several species from the Kyphosus genus. Cases have been documented from *Sarpa salpa* as well. Poisoning symptoms are similar to LSD including auditory and visual hallucinations, exact toxin unknown.

Illusion: A distorted or misinterpretion of reality.

Imaginary: Does not mimic real perception and is under voluntary control.

Indole: An organic aromatic chemical compound consisting of a six carbon benzene ring that is infused with a five carbon nitrogen ring. It is a major component of tryptophan, which can eventually turn into the neurotransmitter serotonin.

LSD: D-Lysergic Acid Diethylamide - synthetic chemical which, when taken orally or, less commonly, in the lining of an eyelid or nostril, is the most potent hallucinogen known to the common public.

Nervous system- organ system containing a network of specialized cells called neurons that coordinate the actions and transmit signals between different parts of the body.

Neuroblastoma assay A rotary bioreactor culture, to evaluate and characterize the cell-specific, in vitro behavior of neuroblastoma cell lines.

Neurotoxin - An external chemical which when presented to the nervous system, acts as a poison. It works by inhibiting the function of the neurons. Some neurotoxins are temporary, and others cause permanent damage.

Neurotransmitter - A chemical signal released from a nerve, caused by a previous nerve impulse, either from input (via the senses like touch) or output (via the brain).

Pancreatitis: The inflammation of the pancreas; usually marked by abdominal pain.

Pathogens: A microbe or microorganism such as a virus, bacterium, prion, or fungus that can cause diseases in its animal or plant host.

Pathological Interpretation: Analysis and unravelling the effect of a disease or an illness on an individual using currently acceptable research and techniques.

Peripheral Nervous System: The nervous system consists of the brain, spinal cord, and a complex network of neurons. This system is responsible for sending, receiving, and interpreting information from all parts of the body.

Phytoplankton: The collection of small or microscopic organisms that float or drift in great numbers in fresh or salt water, especially at or near the surface, and serve as food for fish and other larger organisms.

Pseudo hallucination: Does not mimic real perception, but is not under voluntary control.

Psychoactive : Any chemical substance that alters brain function, whether it be mood, perception, and or consciousness.

Psychotropic: Aaffecting mental activity, behavior, or perception, as a mood-altering drug

Schizophrenia:Any of a group of psychiatric disorder characterized by withdrawal from reality, illogical patterns of thinking, delusions, hallucinations and psychotic behaviour..

Scombroid poisoning: A foodborne illness that results from eating spoiled (decayed) fish. It is the second most common type of seafood poisoning, second only to ciguatera. It is often missed because it resembles an allergic reaction. It is most commonly reported with mackerel, tuna, mahi-mahi, bonito, sardines, anchovies, and related species of fish that were inadequately refrigerated or preserved after being caught. Scombroid syndrome can result from inappropriate handling of fish during storage or processing. One of the toxic agents implicated in scombroid poisoning is histamine.

Sea Bream: A deep-bodied marine fish that resembles the freshwater bream, in particular.

Serotonin : A natural hormone produced in the pineal gland in the brain. It is crucial hormone in that it allows numerous functions in the human body including control of appetite, sleep, mood, behaviour, muscle contraction, and many other things. Low levels of serotonin would be the cause of depression, and most anti-depressant drugs promote the production of more serotonin. Psychoactive drugs cause the mass production, or release of serotonin all at once, to create a hallucination, which is often followed by minor depression for a few days until the pineal gland has restored the normal serotonin levels.

Synapses: A nerve junction that permits a neuron to pass an electrical or chemical signal to another cell. The cell membranes are connected by channels that are capable of passing electrical current, causing voltage changes in the presynaptic cell to induce voltage changes in the postsynaptic cell.

Tetrodotoxin: A highly lethal neurotoxin found in certain puffer fish and in newts of the genus *Taricha* .

Toxin: A poisonous substance, especially one produced by a living organism.

Ubiquitous: An adjective describing the universal presence or omnipresence of something.

Unsaturated fatty acids: Fatty acid molecules with at least one double bond in the carbon chainave an important and critical role in the proper function of human cell tissue.

References

Aligizaki, K.; Nikolaidis, G. 2008. Morphological identification of two tropical dinoflagellates of the genera *Gambierdiscus* and *Sinophysis* in the Mediterranean Sea. *Journal of Biological Research-Thessaloniki*, 9, 75-82.

Bagnis, R.; Berglund, F.; Elias, P.S.; van Esch, G.J.; Halstead, B.W.; Kojima, K. 1970. Problems of Toxicants in Marine Food Products: 1. Marine Biotoxins. Bulletin of the World Health Organization, 42, 69-88.

Bhakuni, D .S. and Rawat, D. S. 2005. Bioactive Marine Natural Products. Springer, New York.

Bibek, R.; Bhunia, A. 2008. Fundamental Food Microbiology, Fourth Edition. Boca Raton, FL:CRC Press - Taylor & Francis Group, LLC.

Chaves, O.; Barbosa-Filho, J.M.;de Athayde-Filho, P. F.; de Oliveira Santos, B. V.; Alexandre-Moreira, M .S. 2009. The Antinociceptive and Anti-Inflammatory Activities of Caulerpin, a Bisindole Alkaloid Isolated from Seaweeds of the Genus *Caulerpa*. *Marine Drugs*, 7, 689-704.

Fernández-Ortega, J. F.; Santos, J. M.; Herrera-Gutiérrez, M. E.; Fernández-Sánchez, V.; Loureo, P. R.; Rancaño, A. A., *et al*. 2010. Seafood Intoxication byTetrodotoxin: First Case in Europe. *The Journal of Emergency Medicine*. Elsevier Inc.

Glennon, R. A.; Rosecrans, J. A. 1981. Speculations on the Mechanism of Action of Hallucinogenic Indolealkylamines. *Neuroscience and Biobehavioral Reviews*, 5, 197-207.

Güven, K. C.; Percot, A.; Sezik, E. 2010. Alkaloids in Marine Algae. *Marine Drugs*, 8, 269-284.

de Haro, L.; Pommier, P.; and Valli, M. 2003. Emergence of Imported Ciguatera in Europe: Report of 18 cases at the Poison Control Centre of Marseille. *Clinical Toxicology*, 41, 927-930.

de Haro, L.; and Pommier, P. 2006. Hallucinatory Fish Poisoning (Ichthyoallyeinotoximsm): Two case Reports from the Western Mediterranean and Literature Review. *Clinical Toxicology*, 44, 185-188.

Health-Care-Clinic.com (2011). Hallucination-Hallucination symptom, treatment, causes. Retrieved 18th July, 2011 from http://www.health-care-clinic.com/family-health/h/hallucination.htm

Hungerford, J. M. 2010. Scombroid poisoning: A review. *Toxicon*, Elsevier Inc.

Mahowald, M. W.; Woods, S. R., and Schenck, C. H. 1998. Sleeping Dreams, Waking Hallucinations, and the Central Nervous System. *Dreaming*, 8(2), 89-102.

Moreira, M .S. 2009. The Antinociceptive and Anti-Inflammatory Activities of Caulerpin, a Bisindole Alkaloid Isolated from Seaweeds of the Genus *Caulerpa*. *Marine Drugs*, 7, 689-704.

Ohayon, M. M. 2000. Prevalence of hallucinations and their pathological association in the general population. *Psychiatry Research*, 97(2-3), 153-164.

Paul, V. J.; Littler, M. M.; Littler, D .S. and Fenical, W. 1987. Evidence for chemical defense in tropical green alga *Caulerpa ashmeadii* (Caulerpaceae: Chlorophyta): Isolation of New Bioactive Sesquiterpenoids. *Journal of Chemical Ecology*, 13(5), 1171-1185.

Phan, V.; Ersboll, A.; Do, D.; Dalsgaard, A. 2010. Raw-fish eating behaviour and fishorne zoonotic trematode infection in people of northern Vietnam. *Foodborne Pathogens and Disease* 8(2):255-259.

Sabry, F. 2010. Hallucinations Are More Frequent Than We Think. Retrieved 18th July, 2011 form http://ezinearticles.com/?Hallucinations-Are-More-Frequent-Than-We-Think&id=6038963

De Souza, E, T.; de Lira, D. P. de Queiroz, A.C.; da Silva, D. J. C.; de Aquino, A. B.; Campessato Mella, E.A.; Lorenzo, V.P. de Miranda, G.E.C.; de Araújo-Júnior, J.X.; de Oliveira Chaves, *et al.* M. 2009. The Antinociceptive and Anti-Inflammatory Activities of Caulerpin, a Bisindole Alkaloid Isolated from Seaweeds of the Genus *Caulerpa. Marine Drugs*, 7(4), 689-704.

Stewart, I.; Eaglesham, G. K.; Poole,S.; Graham, G.; Paulo, C.; Wickramasinghe, W., *et al.* 2010. Establishing a public health analytical service based on chemical methods for detecting and quantifying Pacific ciguatoxin in fish samples. *Toxicon,* Elsevier Ltd.

Sua, S .C.; Choua, S.S.; Changa, P. C.; and Hwang, D. F. 2000. Determination of biogenic amines in fish implicated in food poisoning by micellar electrokinetic capillary chromatography. *Journal of Chromatography B*, 749, 163-169.

Vidal, J. P.; Laurent, D.; Kabore, S. A.; Rechencq, E.; Boucard, M.; Girard, J.P.; Escale, R.; and Rossi, J. C. 1984. Caulerpin, Caulerpicin, *Caulerpa scalpelliformis*: *Comparative Acute Toxicity Study. Botanica Marina*, 27, 533-537.

§10:

Sweet dreams are made of cheese....

Stilton cheese that is... remix!

It has been said that "cheese is milk's leap towards immortality" but with its ability to cause and influence the dreams of connoisseurs, this immortality may have already been achieved. Vivid and bizarre dreams such as a vegetarian crocodile upset because it could not eat children, a dinner party where guests are traded for camels or a party in an insane asylum are just some of the many dreams experienced by people after eating British Stilton before they sleep.

'To sleep, per chance to dream', a quote from the infamous Shakespearian play Hamlet appropriately describes our incredible fascination with dreams. It is believed that dreams are a window into a world that exists on a different level of consciousness than we experience while we are awake. While everyone enters this dream world, it is a world that is unique to each person. Dreams may happen during any of the four stages of the sleep cycle with the last stage, REM sleep, being the most vivid and memorable. REM sleep occurs 90-100 minutes after the onset of sleep. Dreams draw on different types of stored memory in the brain, therefore ensuring that no two people ever have the same dream. Since dreams are so unique to each person, reflecting individual thoughts, feeling, fears, desires, and belief systems, dreams have been used and studied by many disciplines including psychology, pharmacology, neurology, theology, medicine, and nutrition.

Many remarkable cross cultural variations are seen in beliefs surrounding the nature and importance of dreams. In most modern Western cultures dreams are rarely seen as predictors of the future or as significant features of one person. In many native cultures in North America and Australia, however, dreams are viewed to be very important. The Native American culture perceive their dreams as signs and visions of the future, guiding them to their identity and showing them what future actions should be taken. Across most Australian Aboriginal tribes dreams are believed to determine or describe their lives, culture, and relationships to their environment and people, enlightening and enriching their spiritual identity. There is a universal belief across all of the tribes on 'Dreamtime', viewed in four facets: the beginning of all things; the life and influence of the ancestors; the way of life and death; and sources of power in life. On the other hand, the Arapesh of New Guinea believe dreams to be literal experience of an individual's drifting soul, and an erotic dream may be viewed as equivalent to adultery in which the husband's wife would be regarded as cuckolded. In yet other cultures dreams are seen as ways to connect to the spiritual world or windows into the future. In Malaysia, for example, the Senoi tribes have a morning ritual of sitting down together and talking about their dreams from the previous night, discussing how they can defeat the bad omens that arise while they were sleeping. It is seen as essential to talk about their dreams before moving on with their daily lives. Dream interpretations are deemed to be inconsistent across culture. With the advancement in scientific studies (neuroscience in particular), however, dream interpretation has been made possible to some extent, although depending on which side of the argument you're on. This fact has therefore posed many challenges when used by various scientific disciplines to make more universal sense of dreams and what they may indicate.

Dreams are important in all cultures around the world, and sleep disturbances such as the inability to fall asleep or stay asleep, prevent normal dreaming and are mostly considered in negative terms by most cultures and peoples. To alleviate these undesirable sleep disturbances, many cultures have historically used ancient traditional medicine to induce sleep and even produce dreams from natural plant based substances. These plants include; Valerian (*Valeriana officinalis, L*) a plant that is used as a sedative, St. John's Wort (*Hypericum perforatum, L.*) used for treating depression, Chamomile a daisy like flower has been known to produce sleep and treat stress, Mugwort, (*Artemisia vulgaris, L.*) a plant used for relaxation and many others. In 'modern' society, 'dietary' supplements in pill, powders, or liquid forms are sold beside milk and bread, although the effectiveness and safety of some of these supplements are questionable.

Most cultures and societies normally allow dreams to develop naturally. Other cultures naturally use "dream-inducing" herbs to enhance the feeling of lucid dreaming. Lucid dreaming is "a dream in which the dreamer, while dreaming, is aware that she/he is dreaming" (Schredl & Erlacher, November). Dream inducing herbs also have the power to alter and influence dreams. The dreamers blend; a combination of dream herbs have the ability to experience meaningful dreams with insight, or have dreams that are extremely entertaining (Turner). The Chontal Indians of Mexico used a plant-Calea Zacatechichi that allowed them to obtain divinatory message through dreaming. This plant could be consumed in tea or smoked and provides a light hypnotic state for the user.

Other cultures use psychoactive compounds to enhance reality. Amazon Indians have been using the compound Harmaline, which is located in the bark of several different plant species in the area. The result is a drink that has been used in religious rituals since pre-historic times. Harmaline is a reversible inhibitor of MAO-A and inhibiting this enzyme decreases the rate cells are able to oxidize monoamines, thereby contributing to Harmaline's stimulating effect on the central nervous system. Tribes in the Congo have used the plant Ibogaine for similar reasons. Ibogaine is a psychoactive alkaloid naturally occurring in the root bark of the West African shrub Ibogaine. In large doses Ibogaine is able to induce psychedelic states. Ibogaine is an agonist for the 5-HTa receptor; 5-HT agonists such as LSD activate these receptors to produce psychoactive effects. Both these drugs have some possible therapeutic effects. Ibogaine for example, when taken in small doses is capable of reducing withdrawal symptoms from opiates and can therefore reduce substance-related cravings. Harmaline research has shown to act as a vasorelaxant.

Still today, many legal antipsychotic drugs can cause not only increased dream vividness but also increase dream recall. Antipsychotic drugs are used to act against psychotic illnesses which effect people who are out of touch with reality. These types of drugs are not meant to cure the illness, but make them milder. Dopamine agonists such as the monoamine oxidase inhibitors (MAOIs) are a powerful group of antidepressant drugs used to treat the symptoms of Parkinson's disease but are used as a last resort because, unfortunately, they also induce vivid dreams, often sexual in nature. Symptoms of Parkinson's disease include tremor, rigidity and postural instability. Dopamine agonist drugs act like dopamine to stimulate your nerve cells. Parkinson's medications known as dopamine agonists control many of the symptoms of Parkinson's disease by mimicking the actions that dopamine is responsible for. Today people using opioid painkillers (*e.g.* morphine methadone, oxycodone, and codeine) often report vivid realistic dreams which purportedly are more effective during its first use. Users may sometimes even become addicted not only to the drug itself but also to the vivid dreams that result from its use. Addiction can be lethal as a reportedly 37,000 Americans died from overdose in the year 2006. It is interesting to note that morphine was named after Morpheus, the Greek god of sleep and dreams.

Likewise many other drugs utilized to treat other maladies can also intensify dreams. There are no drug treatments available that can eliminate Alzheimer's disease completely; however, medications have been manufactured to improve symptoms or slow the progression of the disease in some patients. Some medications used in the treatment of Alzheimer's disease not only increases the frequency of vivid dreams but can cause patients to recall the dream with more ease. They are able to verbally describe the dream, or write it down on paper. Such medication may also cause dreams to be bizarre, usually described through misrepresentations or distortional viewpoints. Drugs used in hypertension management aid in alleviating symptoms and bringing blood pressure back to an acceptable level. These are called beta–blockers, which can be used to repress convulsions, treat depression, Alzheimer's disease and ALS (Lou Gehrig's disease in North America). Beta-blockers have the ability to affect the nature of the dream. Other drugs used to help in the cessation of smoking, as well as testosterone, can induce barbaric and unpleasant nightmares. Synthetic drugs (manufactured or chemically altered unsafe drugs such as LSD or meth), or naturally found drugs harvested from plants (marijuana) are not the only substances that can trigger obscure dreams, but foods consumed on a regular basis may contain psychoactive compounds that trigger vivid and cryptic dreams. Foods with high protein content like meat, dairy and soy which regularly undergo aging, fermentation, pickling or smoking, tend to be high in dream inducing substances. For example, well-aged cheeses such as Stilton are full of flavour and also contain psychoactive agents that can influence dreams. Stilton cheese contains the relaxant tryptophan, which can get you naturally high.

The mild tasting Stilton cheese (compared to other blue cheeses) has affectionately been given the title "The King of English Cheeses". This title does not only describe its place in British cheese history and culture but can equally be used to describe the lucid and vivid dreams it can induce after the consumption of a mere 20 grams just before bedtime. This is not, however, a phenomenon that just occurs with Stilton cheese. A study conducted in 2005 demonstrated that different types of cheese may cause different types of dreams, good or bad, but Stilton cheese can cause quite unusual dreams (Sweet Dreams Are Made Of Cheese, 2005). Stilton is a member of the blue veined cheese family which includes other illustrious blue cheeses including Roquefort (France), Gorgonzola (Italy), Danablu (Denmark), and Maytag Blue (USA), is an internally ripened cheese. This blue veined cheese with dreamy side effects acquired its name in the 18th century, named after the town of Stilton (Cambridgeshire, England) just north of London. The cheese ironically was not made in the town; the name came to be as it was first sold in the town of Stilton. No single person actually invented the current Stilton cheese, its form was evolved. The cheese started off being a pressed, cooked cream cheese and later developed to be the unpressed semi-hard blue veined cheese we have today.

Stilton cheese, although not made in Stilton got its name from travelers on their way from London to York as they would stop to refresh themselves and their horses in the town of Stilton. In 1722, William Stukeley made the first mention of Stilton cheese in a letter. One year later, Daniel Defoe a travel writer, referred to Stilton cheese as "English Parmesan," indicating its high regard and reputation. London and Edinburgh soon became a trading post which Cooper Thornhill used to his advantage. He was the owner of a small inn called "The Bell Inn" where he sold local cheeses to travelers passing through and into London. Over time, the demand for cheese grew large, Cooper wanted to expand the types of cheeses he sold and so in 1743 he made a deal with a cheese-maker named Frances Pawlett. Together Cooper Thornhill and Frances Pawlett were accountable for the initial success of Stilton Cheese and the further development of a recipe that is still in use today. Owing to the psychoactive and drug like properties of the cheese, his exclusive rights would be comparable to some of our modern pharmaceutical firms who have exclusive rights to make and sell certain drugs. Not only did Thornhill sell great amounts of Stilton cheese to travelers on their way to the north of England, he helped to spread the Stilton cheese and its reputation far and wide throughout England.

About a decade later Thornhill, no longer able to keep up with demand, made an exclusive commercial arrangement with Francis Pawlett (Paulet), a local woman and skilled cheese maker in Leicestershire. Using milk produced on local farms, she invented innovative manufacturing techniques such as ceramic pipes or cylinders with holes in them which allowed the un-pressed cheese to drain and mature while exposed to the air, enhancing the growth of the blue-green mould. In modern times, the cheese is stuck through with stainless steel needles in order to allow bacterial growth and air exposure. There is a certain irony that Stilton cheese can no longer be produced in Stilton due to regulations that state that cheese can only be called Stilton cheese if it is produced with milk from Derbyshire, Leicestershire, and Nottinghamshire (Stilton does not fall into these counties). The reason for these regulations of course is to preserve Stilton's cheese distinct taste because the specific strain of airborne fungus (*Penicillium roqueforti*) that produces the taste can only be found in those parts of the world. But *P. roqueforti* itself is widespread and used in the production of many blue cheeses around the world. It is not known how the *P. roqueforti* fungus mould initially 'found' a niche in the cheese. If it was by deliberate brushing or by chance, *e.g.* the cheese cracking as it dried and airborne spores set 'up shop' so to speak. Pawlett was also the first person to standardize the making and processing of the cheese including its final quality, colour, size and shape which have become the standards for the cheese until the present time.

For almost two centuries, there have been very few written references about Stilton as it seems to have fallen asleep. In 1996, Stilton cheese woke up, and gained both national and international attention as the European Union granted the blue veined and less popular, white veined Stilton cheeses, its Protected Designation of Origin (PDO) status. This designation has also been granted to other British foods such as Melton Mowbray pork pies (Leicestershire), Jersey Red potatoes (Jersey), and Cornish Clotted Cream (Cornwall). The PDO designation ensures that consumers are purchasing a genuine food product made in the traditional manner. In the case of Stilton, there are many similar cheeses so this verification is important. Only six licensed dairies produce it, with pasteurized milk from three historically associated counties. A Stilton wheel weighs 7.7 kilograms and requires 82 litres of milk, and a minimum of nine weeks for it to mature and produce a sharp flavour. The more desirable buttery flavour takes another six weeks! According to its PDO designation, it must be made in the traditional cylindrical shape with its blue veins radiating from the center and must also form its wrinkled 'crust' naturally. The cheese must remain un-pressed, knitting together under its own weight causing its texture to become loose, crumbly, and flaky; characteristics which also encourage mould growth. This texture allows carbon dioxide to escape and oxygen to enter. Stilton's unique flavour with its sharp aftertaste, open texture, and creamy mouth feel is a cheese that is enjoyed anytime but especially at Christmas with a glass of good port. Considering that Stilton cheese can also induce dreams that are very dramatic and bizarre but at the same time keeps the dreamer self-aware it isn't surprising that it is in high demand around the world.

So, are you cheesed off with not having a clear and interesting 'night life'? Interested in a little excitement while sleeping? In England, and perhaps elsewhere as well, there is an old belief that eating cheese before bedtime will result in nightmares. To disprove this old belief and also to promote the consumption of British cheese, The British Cheese Board decided to investigate the effect of cheese on sleep phenomena such as the quality of sleep and incidences of both dreams and nightmares in a study conducted in 2005. To say the least, The Cheese Board was taken by quite a surprise with the results! This semi-scientific investigation asked 200 people (100 men, 100 women) to consume a 20 gram (just over 1Tbsp) piece of pre-determined cheese (Stilton, aged Cheddar, Red Leicester, British Brie, Lancashire, or Cheshire)

30 minutes before bedtime, with an equal number of people in each group. Each morning, the participants recorded the type of sleep and the dreams that they had experienced during the night. The good news is that none of the cheeses were reported to induce nightmares in the participants although the type of cheese seemed to affect the type of dreams along with some interesting gender differences. If you are interested in changing careers, then eat Lancashire before you go to bed! British Brie induced relaxing dreams in women but men experienced odd, obscure dreams such as having a drunken conversation with a dog. If you like celebrities, then eating Cheddar is for you! On the other hand, nostalgic dreams tended to be reported by participants eating red Leicester. The two most surprising cheeses, however, were Cheshire and Stilton. Over 50% of the Cheshire cheese participants experienced dreamless and uneventful whereas Stilton participants experienced quite the opposite effect. Compared to the other five cheeses, the Stilton cheese seemed to induce very peculiar dreams indeed! After eating a mere 20 gram serving of Stilton before bedtime, 75% of men and 85% of women experienced 'odd and vivid' dreams such as talking with soft toys, an upset vegetarian crocodile, and the like.

This particular study failed to eliminate as many external factors as possible. The cheese study did not use a control group to compare the findings nor did they use a Stilton cheese look-a-like. The participants and investigators personal beliefs, traditions and other factors could have all influenced the results of the study. In a strong study, investigators would have participants consuming all of the cheeses in a pre-determined order between periods of non-cheese consumption. Despite these limitations, this study on Stilton cheese is interesting and according to current experimental designs, there should be further investigations.

The clarity and vividness of dreams experienced by the Stilton participants are thought to be caused by an increase in the brain's tryptophan levels. Stilton cheese is high in protein but has an extremely low amount of tryptophan compared to other types of cheeses surveyed by the USDA. The British Cheese Board claims that the vivid dreams induced by Stilton cheese is due to the amount of tryptophan as it is the precursor for the relaxant neurotransmitter Serotonin, which plays a role in awareness and sense of reality. If the amount of tryptophan in Stilton cheese was the cause of the vivid dreams, the proteins in the cheese would be digested in both the stomach and the small intestine. The proteins would be further broken down into smaller groups of amino acids which are the building blocks of protein. After digestion they would enter the bloodstream and be transported throughout the body. As the blood circulates to the brain, some of the tryptophan crosses into the central nervous system across the blood/brain barrier. Tryptophan is then converted into the serotonin and the B vitamin, niacin. Darkness induces the conversion of serotonin into melatonin, which makes sleep easier and increases the amount of REM sleep. During REM sleep most people experience vivid dreams caused by brain chemicals stimulating different areas of the brain. But at this low amount, tryptophan does not likely produce an effect in Stilton cheese unless the information was incorrectly printed. Other scientific studies on European blue veined cheeses show that Stilton cheese is not exceptionally high in tryptophan; rather it has one of the lowest amounts of tryptophan. The USDA conducted a study stating that protein levels in dairy products decrease as moisture levels increase. Since Stilton cheese has a moisture content of 38% and it has an average amount of protein at 23.7%, it would not be expected to have high amounts of tryptophan.

The increased occurrence of clear and vivid dreams is also believed to be affected by bacterial and fungal cultures in cheese. The greatest effects on inducing dreams involve very ripe, mature, or mouldy cheeses. During cheese maturation, the activity of these bacterial and fungal cultures produces relatively large amounts of biogenic amines. In some cases, it can be these compounds directly, or their metabolites which influence dreaming. Some of these biogenic amines have psychoactive properties, affecting mind or mental processes. High amounts of biogenic amines, tryptamine (chemically related to tryptophan) and tyramine, have been found in a number of aged and dry cheeses, as well as in other foods which have been fermented with a group of bacteria (lactic acid bacteria, (LAB)). Interestingly, studies on blue veined cheese, such as Stilton, found the highest levels of tyramine in the middle of the cheese. In the case of Stilton, this would indeed make sense as the blue-green *P. roqueforti* veins are concentrated in the centre and spread outwards. Tryptamine, however, showed the opposite concentration gradient. Aged, fermented, or 'spoiled' protein rich foods such as cheese and cured meats generally contain more Tyramine. and should be avoided by people taking Monoamine Oxidase Inhibitors (MAOIs) or some antidepressants, as these prevent Tyramine metabolism leading to sudden increase in hormones dopamine, epinephrine, and Norepinephrine which can cause dangerously high blood pressure (hypertensive crisis) and heart palpitations (True Star Health, 2012).

Most varieties of cheese, including Stilton, Danish Blue, French Roquefort, Parmesan, Romano, Asiago, and aged Cheddar, contain a chemical called tyramine which is present in all aged, smoked, fermented, or pickled foods as well as alcoholic beverages. Tyramine acts as a dopamine which influences the way the brain behaves and affects the learning, attention, movement, pain and pleasure, and arousal relating to human beings. This causes the release of another chemical (norepinephrine) that increases the amount of time that is spent in deep sleep, where more dreaming will occur. The longer time spent in deep sleep, the more time there will be for dreams to occur. The increases in the chemical levels in the brain caused by dopamine are maximized during deep sleep which explains the bizarreness of the dreams that result from eating a small piece of Stilton cheese shortly before bedtime.

If tryptophan is the reason for increased incidences of more lucid, vivid dreams as claimed by The British Cheese board, then what about warm milk before bedtime? While milk contains tryptophan, it does not contain enough to induce sleep or dreaming in most people. If the tryptophan content is not responsible then is it the temperature? According to studies, it does not seem that sleep caused by warm milk is due to the increased temperature either. Studies have shown that to induce sleep by warmth, it is better to warm the skin directly, take note of a cat seeking, and sleeping, in warm places such as a sunny window. The consumption of warm milk is not enough to raise the skin temperature from the inside although it may provide a 'good in your tummy' feeling. So why does warm milk seem to work? Scientists believe that the calcium, carbohydrate, and tryptophan in the milk help the brain to manufacture serotonin. One study by researchers at the Massachusetts Institute of Technology in 2003, however, showed that eating protein-rich foods like milk decreased the ability of tryptophan to enter the brain. The trick, the study showed, is to eat foods high in carbohydrates which stimulate the release of insulin. Insulin, in turn, makes it easier for tryptophan to enter the brain. This is the reason that foods which are high in calcium and carbohydrates and medium to low-protein can help induce sleep. Humans also have a strong psychological association with warm milk which was established at birth, much like tucking into bed with our favourite teddy bear or blanket.

Tryptophan is found in foods such as fluid milk and cheese and this amino acid is able to cross the blood brain barrier; a semi-permeable membrane preventing undesirable substances from entering the brain. Tryptophan-containing foods cross the blood brain barrier in greater amounts if they are consumed at the same time as complex carbohydrates (*e.g.* cereal, brown rice). When carbohydrates are ingested, the body releases a hormone called insulin that signals the body to take up glucose, fatty acids, and amino acids thereby clearing the bloodstream of glucose, fatty acids, and all amino acids with the exception of tryptophan. The increase in concentration of tryptophan in the blood stream allows for easier absorption across the blood brain barrier. Once in the brain, tryptophan has a calming effect which helps an individual relax, making sleep come easier. As with all meals, everything in moderation though as large meals, high protein or high fat meals before bedtime can not only make falling asleep more difficult but may also cause an increase in weight gain and unpleasant dreams. An added bonus, the increase in blood sugar may also help to maintain the state of sleep as sometimes people wake up in the middle of the night as a result of too low blood sugar.

If milk is unable to induce sleep and dreaming, then why can cheese? Compared to fluid milk, all cheeses have higher protein content, as they are concentrated milk products. In the case of Stilton, it takes a whopping 5 liters of milk to make one pound of cheese as most of the water is removed concentrating the proteins and fats. Different types of bacteria and mold are used when making aged cheese like Stilton. These bacteria and mold are involved in biochemical reactions that act to age the cheese in its maturation period. Some studies have also shown that foods such as Stilton cheese fermented by lactic acid bacteria (LAB) will have a higher amount of the amino acid tyramine. This amino acid acts to release the protein dopamine in the brain, which contributes to brain function. The bacteria in cheese will act to break down protein to their free amino acids in a process called proteolysis. While higher microbial activity frees more amino acids from proteins during Stilton maturation, but tryptophan has not been shown not to be one of them.

There is a common misconception that fatigue after a turkey dinner is due solely to its tryptophan content. Tryptophan is an essential amino acid, used as a precursor to forming serotonin, which is a neurotransmitter responsible for regulating moods, appetite, and sleep. When comparing different food products, turkey contains 0.24 g per 100 g while in comparison to cheese; approximately 0.32 g per 100 g is present. People do not usually get overly sleepy after eating other high protein foods and this helps in disproving the myth that tryptophan is the primary culprit responsible for causing fatigue. During the holidays people ingest large amounts of food, specifically those consisting of high concentrations of carbohydrates. Carbohydrates contain large amounts of sugar, also known as glucose that enters the blood stream. Consequently the body needs to go through a series of steps to remove this excess glucose, thus the pancreas begins releasing insulin. One theory for the cause of drowsiness following a large high carbohydrate meal is that when too much insulin is released too much glucose is removed; therefore individuals get drowsy due to the lack of glucose in their blood. Therefore, the more carbohydrates people consume, the more insulin secreted and the more likely they will feel drowsy.

The exact science is not yet known as to why Stilton cheese is able to alter your sleeping patterns, but the fact that it can is undisputable. Contributing factors include the presence of tryptophan, which is able to cross the blood brain barrier. Eventually it is converted to melatonin, a known hormone that increases REM cycles as well as aids in actual deed of falling asleep. The environment that this delightfully loose, flakey and mouldy blue cheese is created as well as the use of LAB promotes vast microbial activity whose metabolites act as dopamine for the mind. Dopamine, a blessing straight from the gods above in the form of a neurotransmitter is related to feelings of pleasure, pain, attention and sexual arousal to name a few. The future of

Stitlon's psychoactive potential could be intriguing as these phenomena leak out of the scientific community into society and into the hands of mad marketers looking to tip off the next 'big' nightlife craze. The bottom line is to eat well aged cheeses and other fermented/aged foods like Stilton cheese if you want to sleep and have some exciting night time 'entertainment'. If, however, you wish to stay awake to engage in other night time activities, please refrain from eating Stilton ... your partner will thank you profusely!

Glossary

Alleviate: To make easier, endure.

ALS (Amyotrophic lateral sclerosis or Lou Gehrig's Disease): A medical condition characterized by the loss of motor neurons resulting in a complete cessation of bodily movements.

Alzheimer's disease: Loss of neurons in the brain that cause mental deterioration.

Amino Acids: The small subunits that make up protein.

Antipsychotic drugs: Medication that is mainly used to manage delusions, hallucinations and disordered thoughts mostly in schizophrenia and bipolar disorder.

Beta-blockers: Biological molecules which act on cardiac or other peripheral vasculature to treat hypertension, depression, convulsions, Alzheimer's disease, and ALS.

Biogenic: Naturally occurring from plants, animals, or bacterial cultures.

Biogenic amines: Naturally occurring amines (nitrogen-containing group) derived by enzymatic activity that consists of an amine group (nitrogen with lone pair of electrons).

Blood Brain Barrier: A protective mechanism that alters the permeability of the brain's capillaries, so that some substances are prevented from entering brain tissue, while other substances are allowed to freely enter.

British Cheese Board: "the voice of British cheese". This group is dedicated to educating the British public about eating cheese as part of a balanced diet http://www.britishcheese.com/home).

British Stilton: A blue cheese from Britain known for its crumbly texture and flavour.

CaleaZactechichi: A dream herb gives the user the feeling of making dreams more vivid and realistic, with the possibility of helping dreamers achieve lucidity.

Central Nervous System: The part of the nervous system that contains the brain and spinal cord.

Connoisseurs: A person with knowledge and expertise in their field.

Convulsions: A medical condition resulting from contracting body muscles, resulting in uncontrolled shaking of the body.

Cuckolded: A derogatory term for a man who has an unfaithful wife.

Depression: A mental condition associated with a lack of energy, difficulty concentrating and/or lack of interest in life.

Divination: Attempting to gain insight of future events or discover "hidden" messages through a supernatural means.

Dopamine: A simple organic chemical that plays a number of important roles in physiological functions. Dopamine levels in the brain increase with reward, with certain drugs also increase levels.

Dopamine agonists: Medication that activates dopamine receptors when there is no dopamine present to eventually lead to changes in gene transcription by activating pathways through a dopamine receptor.

Dream: A progression of thoughts, emotions, images, and sounds produced by and experienced in the brain during sleep.

Facets: An aspect or phase, as of a subject or personality.

Fermentation: Food processing using yeasts, bacteria, and fungal cultures.

Hypertension: Abnormally high blood pressure.

.

Induce: To bring about, produce or cause.

Insomnia: Inability to have sufficient sleep, fall asleep or stay asleep.

Insulin: A hormone secreted by the pancreas that regulates fat and carbohydrate metabolism. It causes the liver, muscle and fat tissue to take the blood glucose and covert it into glycogen, which is then stored in the liver and the muscle.

Lactic Acid Bacteria (LAB): A specific type of bacteria commonly found in decomposing plants and lactic products. This bacterial classification is characterized by having a slight tolerance to acidic conditions.

Lucid Dreaming: A dream in which the dreamer, while dreaming, is aware that she/he is dreaming.

Maturation: The process of becoming mature or reaching the desirable state.

Melatonin: A naturally occurring hormone that is involved in regulating the body's "internal clock."

Metabolite: The intermediates and product of metabolism.

Moisture Content: The measure of the actual amount of water vapour present in the air.

Monoamine neurotransmitters: Endogenous chemicals which transmit signals from a neuron to a target cell (such as dopamine, epinephrine, and norepinephrine).

Monoamine Oxidase Inhibitors: Medicines that relieve certain types of mental depression.

Morphine: Morphine is the naturally occurring opioid in the opium poppy. Its clinical uses are for pain management.

Mouthfeel: Tactile sensation a food gives to the mouth.

Mug Wort: A plant used in herbal remedies, especially used for relaxation.

Neurology: The science of the nerves and the nervous system, especially of the diseases affecting them.

Neuroscience: The scientific study of the nervous system; one of the study branches in biology.

Neurotransmitter: A chemical substance that transmits nerve impulses across a synapse.

Niacin: B vitamin that is crucial for the normal function of the nervous system and the gastrointestinal tract.

Norepinephrine: A neurotransmitter and a hormone that can increase the rate of heart contractions.

Omens: A phenomenon or occurrence regarded as a sign of future happiness or disaster.

Oneirogenic: Producing a dream-like state.

Opioid: An opium-like compound.

Pharmacology: The science dealing with the preparation, uses, and especially the effects of drugs.

Psychoactive compound: A substance that enters the brain and causes a change in normal brain function which can result in changes in behaviour, mood, and perception.

Psychology: The science of the mind or of mental states and processes.
REM: The stage of sleep where the eyes move back and forth erratically, also referred as Delta sleep. This stage is the most restorative part of sleep and majority of dreaming occurs in this stage.

Sedative: A substance that has a soothing, calming or tranquilizing effect.

Serotonin: A hormone and a neurotransmitter that is made from tryptophan. It plays a role in the regulation of mood, sleep, learning and constriction of blood vessels.

St Johns Wort: A plant use for medicinal purposes this includes the treatment of depression, anxiety and/or sleep disorders.

Testosterone: A hormone naturally found in the body or synthetically prepared that stimulate the development of male sex organs, sexual traits and sperm.

Theology: The field of study and analysis that treats of God and of God's attributes and relations to the universe; study of divine things or religious truth; divinity.

Tryptophan: An essential amino acid that acts as a precursor to an important neurotransmitter, serotonin (Vitamin Supplements Guide, 2006).

Tyramine: A colorless crystalline amine found in mistletoe, putrefied animal tissue, certain cheeses, and ergot, or produced synthetically, used as a sympathomimetic agent.

USDA: United States Department of Agriculture.

Valerian: a plant used as a sedative.

References

Anandan, S. 2005. For bizarre dreams, bite into Stilton cheese. The Times of India. Retrieved from http://timesofindia.indiatimes.com/city/hyderabad-times/For-bizarre-dreams-bite-into-Stilton-cheese/articleshow/1238446.cms

Barbara, B. 2004. The Mozart Effect - Metamusic, Memory, Sleep & Quantum Learning. Retrieved from http://childrenofthenewearth.com/. 4(2), 38-45.

Bishop, J. 2011. Psychoactive substances. Science Daily. Retrieved from
http://www.sciencedaily.com/releases/2009/02/090212141158.html

British Cheese Board. 2005. Sweet Dream Are Made Of Cheese. Retrieved from British
Cheese Board http:/www.cheeseboard.co.uk/news.cfm?page_id=240

British Cheese Board - News. 2005. Internet Archive: Wayback Machine. Retrieved from
http://web.archive.org/web/20060115000115/http://www.cheeseboard.co.uk/news.cfm?page_id=
240

Chudler, E.H. 2011. The Blood Brain Barrier. Neuroscience for Kids. Retrieved from
http://faculty.washington.edu/chudler/bbb.html

Crisp, T. 2010. Australian Aborigine Dream Beliefs. Dream Hawk. Retrieved from
http://dreamhawk.com/dream-encyclopedia/australian-aborigine-dream-beliefs/

Department of Justice. 2012. Controlled Drugs and Substances Act 1996. Retrieved from
http://laws-lois.justice.gc.ca/eng/acts/C-38.8/

Dream Research. 2012. Dream Moods. Retrieved from
http://www.dreammoods.com/dreaminformation/dreamresearch.html

Everyday Health. 2009. Long-Term Side Effects of Parkinson's Medication. Retrieved from
http://www.everydayhealth.com/parkinsons-disease/parkinsons-drug-risks.aspx

Fernández-Salguero, J. 2004. Internal Mould-Ripened Cheeses: Characteristics, Composition
and Proteolysis of the Main European Blue Vein Varieties. *Italian Journal of Food Science*,
4(16), 437-446.

Food Democracy. 2008. Sweet dreams: The right foods for a good night sleep.
http://fooddemocracy.wordpress.com/2008/01/28/sweet-dreams-the-right-foods-for-a-good-
nights-sleep

Franklin Institute. 2012. The Human Brain –Proteins. Resources for Science Learning.
Retrieved from http://www.fi.e.du/learn/brain/proteins.html

Heliray, K. 2009. Alzheimer's Disease and Dementia. Medline Plus. Retrieved from
http://www.nlm.nih.gov/medlineplus/alzheimersdisease.html

Hoch, C., and Reynolds, C. 1986. Sleep Disturbances and What to Do About Them. *Geriatric
Nursing*, 7(1), 24-27.

Holden, J. 2011. Food Composition. USDA National Nutrient Database for Standard
Reference retrieved from: http://www.ars.usda.gov/main/site_main.htm?modecode=12-35-45-00

Iboga Therapy House. 2012. About Ibogaine. Retrieved from
http://www.ibogatherapyhouse.net/index.php/about-ibogaine

Jenkins, B. 2009. Does aged cheese contain psychoactive ingredients? All Treatment.
Retrieved from http://www.alltreatment.com/heroin-addiction/heroin-cheese

Kempt, G., Strupff, H. 2010. ALS fact sheet. National Institute of Neurological Disorders and
Stroke. Retrieved from
http://www.ninds.nih.gov/disorders/amyotrophiclateralsclerosis/detail_ALS.htm

Ladero, V.; Fernández, M.; Cuesta, I.; Alvarez, M. 2010. Quantitative detection and
identification of tyramine-producing enterococci and lactobacilli in cheese by multiplex qPCR.
Food Microbiology, 27, 933-939.

Lawlor, J.; Delahunty, C.; Sheehan, J.; Wilkinson, M. 2003. Relationships between sensory
attributes and the volatile compounds, non-volatile and gross compositional constituents of six
blue-type cheeses. *International Dairy Journal*, 13, 481-494.

Markus, C.; Jonkman, L.; Lammers, J.; Deutz, N.; Messer, M. 2005. Evening intake of alpha-
lactalbumin increases plasma tryptophan availability and improves morning alertness and brain
measures of attention. *American Journal of Clinical Nutrition*, 8(5), 1026-1033.

MedicineNet. 2008 . Antipsychotic Medications. Retrieved from
http://www.medicinenet.com/script/main/art.asp?articlekey=26299

MedScape News. 2009. Overdose Deaths Involving Prescription Opioids among Medicaid
Enrollees. Retrieved from http://www.medscape.com/viewarticle/715258

Naranjo, C. 1969. Psycotherapeutic Possibilities of New Fantasy-Enhancing Drugs. *Clinical
Toxicology*, 2(2), 2009-224.

National Institutes of Health. 2012. St John's Wort. Retrieved from
http://nccam.nih.gov/health/stjohnswort

Novella-Rodríguez, S.; Veciana-Nogués, M.T.; Izquierdo-Pulido, M.; and Vidal-Carou, M.C.
2003. Distribution of Biogenic Amines and Polyamines in Cheese. *Journal of Food Science*,
68(3), 750-755.

O'Connor, A. 2007. The Claim: A Glass of Warm Milk Will Help You Get to Sleep at Night.
The New York Times. Retrieved from http://www.nytimes.com/2007/09/04/health/04real.html

Ortega, A. 2011. Can Carbs Cause Drowsiness? Retrieved
from http://www.livestrong.com/article/500465-can-carbs-cause-drowsiness/

Pace-Schott, E.F. 2008. Part 5: Serotonin and dreaming. In, Serotonin and Sleep: Molecular, Functional and Clinical Aspects, Jaime M. Monti, S. R. Pandi-Perumal, Barry L. Jacobs, and David J. Nutt (editors). Birkhäuser Verlag, Basel, (Switzerland). Pages 307-324.

Pagel, J. F. 2006. Chapter 27, The Neuropharmacology of Nightmares. In, Sleep and Sleep Disorders: *A Neuropsychoparmacological Approach*, Malcolm Lader, Daniel P. Cardinali, and S.

R. Pandi-Perumal (editors). Landes Bioscience/Eurekah.com and Springer Science+Business Media.

Pohl, J.; Frohnau, G.; Kerner, W.; Fehm-Wolfsdorf, G. 1997. Symptom awareness is affected by the subjects expectations during insulin-induced hypoglycemia. *Diabetes Care*, 20(5), 796-802.

Schaafsma, G. 2009. Health benefits of milk beyond traditional nutrition. *Australian Journal of Dairy Technology*, 64(1), 113-116.

Sabry Madkor, P. F.; Shalabi, F. S. I.; Metwalli, N. H. 1987. Studies on the ripening of Stilton Cheese Proteolysis. *Food Chemistry*, 25, 13-29.

Schredl, M.; Erlacher, D. 2 004. Lucid dreaming frequency and personality. *Personality and Individual Differences*, 37(7), 1463-1473.

Shaman's Garden. (n.d.). Calea Zacatechichi (Dream Herb). Retrieved from http://www.shamansgarden.com/p-150-calea-zacatechichi-dream-herb.aspx

Sky News. 2005. Cheese Is Grate For Nice Dreams, Says Study. Retrieved from http://news.sky.com/home/article/13436284

Stilton Cheesemakers' Association. 2012. Stilton cheese: History of Stilton. Retrieved from http://www.stiltoncheese.co.uk/history_of_stilton

Stoners, C. 2009. Legal Things You Can Get High On. Retrieved from http://www.gethigh.com.au/index.php/stoners-chest/legal-things-you-can-get-high-on/

Tedlock, B. 1987. Dreaming and dream research (pp.1-31). Great Britain: Cambridge University Press.